Contents

Get it right

Choose the correct answer.

1. From 0810 hrs to 1340 hrs is
   a) 310 min
   b) 530 min
   c) 330 min

2. The angles of a triangle add up to
   a) 90°
   b) 180°
   c) 360°

3. $\frac{12}{16}$ can be reduced to
   a) $\frac{3}{4}$
   b) $\frac{2}{3}$
   c) $\frac{3}{8}$

4. $1\frac{3}{100}$ is the same as
   a) 1·3
   b) 1·03
   c) 1·003

5. If we add together two acute angles the total will be
   a) $<180°$
   b) $=180°$
   c) $>180°$

6. 327 rounded off to the nearest hundred is
   a) 400
   b) 300
   c) 350

7. 1 metre is the same as
   a) 10 cm
   b) 1000 mm
   c) $\frac{1}{10}$ of a km

8. 3·300 l is
   a) $>3\frac{1}{4}l$
   b) $<3\frac{1}{4}l$
   c) $=3\frac{1}{4}l$

9. 28 × 20 is the same as
   a) 56 × 10
   b) 56 × 40
   c) 14 × 80

10. 1 000 000 is
    a) 1 million
    b) ten thousand
    c) one hundred thousand

11. 520 ÷ 20 is the same as
    a) 260 ÷ 40
    b) 130 ÷ 40
    c) 1040 ÷ 40

12. 0·007 is the same as
    a) $\frac{7}{100}$
    b) $\frac{7}{10}$
    c) $\frac{7}{1000}$

13. The area of this shape is
    a) 24 cm²
    b) 20 cm²
    c) 28 cm²

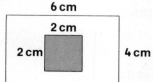

14. The area of this circle $\simeq$
    a) 27 cm²
    b) 9 cm²
    c) 12 cm²

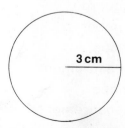

15. $\frac{17}{100}$ is
    a) >0.1
    b) <0.1
    c) $=0.1$

16. 7.38×100 is
    a) <1000
    b) >1000
    c) <100

17. 9962 rounded off to the nearest thousand is
    a) 10000
    b) 1000
    c) 9000

18. If the sides of a square are doubled, its area is
    a) doubled
    b) halved
    c) made 4 times larger

19. 10% of £9·50 is
    a) more than £1
    b) more than £10
    c) less than £1

20. 25% is the same as
    a) $\frac{1}{4}$
    b) $\frac{1}{2}$
    c) $\frac{3}{4}$

21. Which shape always has 4 equal sides?
    a) a rectangle
    b) a rhombus
    c) a trapezium

22. If the sides of a triangle are halved, its perimeter is
    a) half as big
    b) quarter as big
    c) one third as big

23. 7% of 100 is the same as
    a) $\frac{7}{10}$ of 100
    b) $\frac{7}{100}$ of 100
    c) $\frac{1}{7}$ of 100

24. If the sides of a cuboid are doubled, its volume will be
    a) twice as big
    b) four times as big
    c) eight times as big

25. 0.3×100 is the same as
    a) 0.300
    b) 300
    c) 30

26. A million is 100 times greater than
    a) 1000
    b) ten thousand
    c) a hundred thousand

27. Which has the greater area?
    a) the rectangle
    b) the triangle
    c) both the same

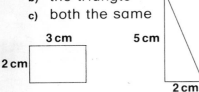

28. Which has the bigger volume?
    a) the cube
    b) the cuboid
    c) both the same

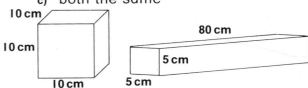

3

Number

Which is greater:

1. $\frac{1}{2}$ of 730 or $\frac{1}{4}$ of 1500?

2. 10% of 320 or 20% of 680?

3. (742 − 399) or (680 − 324)?

4. (0·05 × 100) or (0·62 × 10)?

5. Three hundred and fifty thousand or half a million?

Which is heavier:

6. Four tins of varnish each weighing 397 g, or three tins of varnish each weighing 539 g?

7. Five tubs of putty each weighing 3·25 kg, or nine packets of putty each weighing 1·64 kg?

Which holds more:

8. Six bottles of brush cleaner holding 750 ml each, or three bottles of brush cleaner holding $1\frac{1}{2}$ l each?

9. A box 12 cm long, 9 cm wide and 11 cm high, or a box 10 cm long, 13 cm wide and 8 cm high?

Which costs more:

10. A garden fork costing £16·60 which is reduced by 25%, or a garden fork costing £15 which is reduced by 20%?

11. Tacks weighing $5\frac{1}{2}$ kg costing £1 a kg, or nails weighing $4\frac{1}{2}$ kg costing £1·20 a kg?

Shape

Compasses, protractor

1. Draw a triangle with sides of 50 mm, 38 mm and 42 mm.

Follow these instructions.

Step 1

Draw a line 50 mm long.

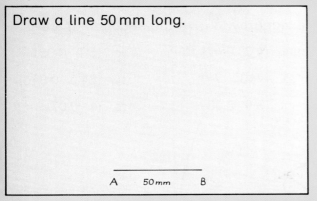

Step 2

Set your compasses at 38 mm, and with compass point on A draw an arc.

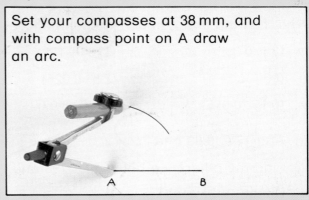

Step 3

Set your compasses at 42 mm. With compass point on B draw an arc to intersect at C.

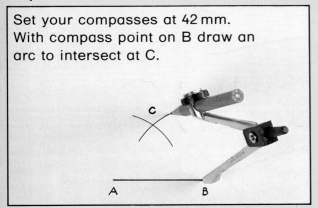

Step 4

Join AC and BC.

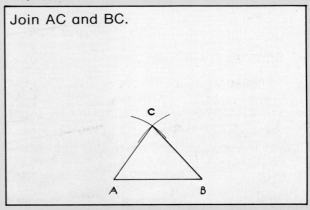

Check the length of each side.
Measure and record the largest angle.
Is it opposite the longest side?

2. Draw these triangles.

	A	B	C	D
Side 1	35 mm	27 mm	53 mm	29 mm
Side 2	58 mm	72 mm	68 mm	54 mm
Side 3	62 mm	53 mm	29 mm	38 mm

Measure and record the largest angle of each triangle.
Is it always opposite the longest side?

Decimals

1. 0.24×10
2. 6.18×100
3. 0.04×100
4. 6.72×10
5. 14.7×100
6. 0.078×1000
7. 5.07×10
8. 0.748×1000
9. $142 \div 10$
10. $16.7 \div 100$
11. $1100 \div 1000$
12. $0.07 \div 10$
13. $2500 \div 100$
14. $90 \div 1000$
15. $2.47 \div 10$
16. $1.9 \div 100$

What has the first number in each pair been divided by to give the second number?

17. (35 0.35)
18. (170 0.17)
19. (4.7 0.47)
20. (5.1 0.051)
21. (650 6.5)
22. (2.5 0.025)
23. (7400 7.4)
24. (84.6 0.846)
25. (0.15 0.015)
26. (8070 8.07)
27. (3.9 0.039)
28. (7 0.07)

29. Add 17.4, 0.83 and 164.4

30. Find the difference between 1.783 and 42.7

31. Divide 24.36 by 7

32. Multiply 0.48 by 9

33. Find the total of 0.786, 1.34 and 26.4

34. Subtract 0.974 from 2.14

35. 17.08×7

36. What number when multiplied by 6 gives an answer of 8.28?

Round these numbers off to the nearest whole number.

37. 4.78
38. 17.9
39. 36.79
40. 0.746
41. 137.8
42. 29.1
43. 5.298
44. 140.5
45. 19.17
46. 8.512
47. 6.623
48. 22.341
49. 245.6
50. 16.683
51. 9.721

Divide these.

52. $25 \div 4$
53. $15 \div 6$
54. $49 \div 4$
55. $35 \div 4$
56. $53 \div 5$
57. $34 \div 8$
58. $17 \div 4$
59. $47 \div 5$
60. $26 \div 8$
61. $31 \div 4$
62. $45 \div 6$
63. $67 \div 4$
64. $13 \div 5$
65. $98 \div 8$
66. $36 \div 8$

$$4.8 \times 7 = \begin{cases} 107.6 \\ \mathbf{33.6} \\ 6.6 \end{cases}$$

This is approximately 5 × 7.
By approximating the answer must be 33·6.

Choose the correct answer by approximating.

1.
$$3.7 \times 6 = \begin{cases} 131.2 \\ 22.2 \\ 4.2 \end{cases}$$

2.
$$5 \times 5.8 = \begin{cases} 29 \\ 7.4 \\ 95.8 \end{cases}$$

3.
$$1.9 \times 6 = \begin{cases} 84.4 \\ 11.4 \\ 2.4 \end{cases}$$

$$6.9 \times 5.4 = \begin{cases} \mathbf{37.26} \\ 129.46 \\ 6.36 \end{cases}$$

This is approximately 7 × 5.
By approximating the answer must be 37·26.

4.
$$2.3 \times 4.2 = \begin{cases} 9.66 \\ 20.76 \\ 0.96 \end{cases}$$

5.
$$7.8 \times 2.5 = \begin{cases} 30.5 \\ 9.4 \\ 19.5 \end{cases}$$

6.
$$3.9 \times 5.6 = \begin{cases} 8.94 \\ 21.84 \\ 0.74 \end{cases}$$

7.
$$8.9 \times 6.7 = \begin{cases} 59.63 \\ 8.43 \\ 224.73 \end{cases}$$

8.
$$3.9 \times 5.4 = \begin{cases} 124.64 \\ 0.74 \\ 21.06 \end{cases}$$

9.
$$6.9 \times 3.6 = \begin{cases} 92.14 \\ 24.84 \\ 3.24 \end{cases}$$

4·3 × 2·4   The approximate answer is 8

```
    4 · 3
 ×  2 · 4
 ─────────
    8 6 0
    1 7 2
 ─────────
 1 0 · 3 2
 ─────────
```

The exact answer is 10·32

Find the exact answers.

10. 7·2 × 6·4

11. 8·3 × 2·5

12. 7·9 × 5·6

13. 8·9 × 5·2

14. 9·7 × 1·8

15. 3·1 × 5·9

16. 6·2 × 8·8

17. 7·4 × 9·6

Ratio

In the picture there are 9 spaceships.
There are 5 pulsar probes and 4 cosmic devils.
The ratio of pulsar probes to cosmic devils is 5 to 4.
It is written 5:4.
The ratio of pulsar probes to cosmic devils is 5:4.

1. What is the ratio of red spaceships to green spaceships?
2. What is the ratio of spaceships without fins to those with fins?

8

These are space people.
The ratio of blue space people to green space people is 4:2.
The ratio of 4:2 can be written more simply as 2:1.
For every 2 blue space people, there is 1 green one.

Below are some space flowers.
Write the ratio of red to orange space flowers in each of these groups.
Write each ratio in its simplest form.

1.

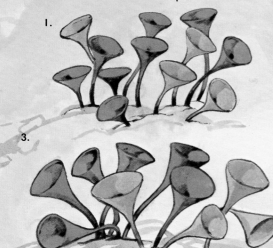

2.

3.

4.

Number

Look at this statement: $4 + 7 + 8$

If it is written as $(4 + 7) + 8$ or $4 + (7 + 8)$

does it make any difference to the answer?

Compare these to see whether the position of the brackets makes any difference.

1. $(4 + 9) + 8$
   $4 + (9 + 8)$

2. $(12 - 3) + 7$
   $12 - (3 + 7)$

3. $(24 - 13) - 7$
   $24 - (13 - 7)$

4. $(9 + 3) + 10$
   $9 + (3 + 10)$

5. $(35 + 14) - 7$
   $35 + (14 - 7)$

6. $(54 - 23) - 16$
   $54 - (23 - 16)$

$14 - 9 + 3 = 2$ This statement is untrue.

$14 - (9 + 3) = 2$ Brackets have made it true.

Put brackets in these to make them true.

7. $20 - 13 - 4 = 3$

8. $25 + 8 - 2 = 31$

9. $36 - 16 + 1 = 21$

10. $44 - 24 - 3 = 23$

11. $50 - 25 - 25 = 50$

12. $50 - 25 - 25 = 0$

13. $23 + 8 - 5 = 26$

14. $37 - 17 + 4 = 16$

15. $37 - 17 + 4 = 24$

Compare each of these to see whether the position of the brackets makes any difference.

16. $(3 \times 8) \times 6$
    $3 \times (8 \times 6)$

17. $(5 \times 8) \div 2$
    $5 \times (8 \div 2)$

18. $(36 \div 6) \div 3$
    $36 \div (6 \div 3)$

19. $(25 \times 4) \div 2$
    $25 \times (4 \div 2)$

20. $(12 \times 8) \times 6$
    $12 \times (8 \times 6)$

21. $(100 \div 10) \div 2$
    $100 \div (10 \div 2)$

Put brackets in these to make them true.

22. $5 \times 4 - 2 = 18$

23. $12 + 3 \times 4 = 60$

24. $14 + 4 \div 2 = 9$

25. $36 \div 4 + 12 = 21$

26. $24 \div 12 \div 3 = 6$

27. $28 - 15 \div 5 = 25$

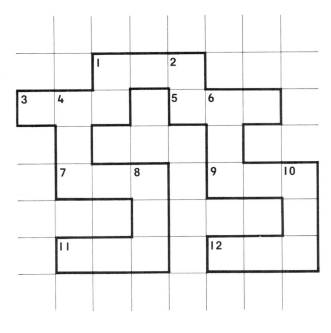

Clues across

1. 8×8

2. Number of edges on a cube.

3. 23×56

4. Number of degrees in a right-angle.

5. Average of 23, 38, 42 and 37.

6. $1\frac{3}{4}$ kg in g.

7. Next prime number after 23.

8. Difference between 4000 and 3962.

9. Area of a 39 cm square in cm².

10. $24 \times \square = 672$

11. $\frac{2}{3}$ of 69

12. Volume of a 12 cm cube in cm³.

Clues across

1. A gross.

3. Next multiple of 14 after 238.

5. $\frac{1}{4}$ of $\square = 93$

7. Product of 24 and 16.

9. Minutes from 11.05 am to 12.48 pm.

11. Number of 5p coins in £5·45.

12. $\frac{1}{2}$ of $3\frac{1}{2}$ metres in cm.

Clues down

1. A dozen.

2. $602 \div \square = 14$

4. Sum of 346 and 227.

6. $\square \div 103 = 7$

8. $\frac{3}{7}$ of 1001

10. Days in 1981.

Ratio

There are 12 fish on the slab.   The ratio of mackerel to sprats is 2:1.
2 out of every 3 fish are mackerel.   So $\frac{2}{3}$ of the 12 fish are mackerel.
1 out of every 3 fish is a sprat.   So $\frac{1}{3}$ of the 12 fish are sprats.
There are 8 mackerel and 4 sprats

1. Copy and complete this table:

No. of fish	Ratio of sprats to mackerel	No. of sprats	No. of mackerel
15	2:1	10	
48	1:3		
70	3:2		
99	4:5		

2. The fishmonger has plaice and halibut on his slab.

   Their total weight is 72 kg.
   The ratio of the weight of plaice to halibut is 5:4.
   What weight of plaice does he have?

3. The fishmonger bought 550 kg of fish from a wholesaler.

   He bought salmon and herring in the ratio of 1:10.
   What weight of herring did he buy?

Number

This table shows the top six football teams of the English League at the end of the 1979–80 season.

	No. of games played	Results playing at home					Results playing away from home					No. of points won
		Won	Drawn	Lost	Goals for	Goals against	Won	Drawn	Lost	Goals for	Goals against	
Liverpool	42	15	6	0	46	8	10	4	7	35	22	60
Man. United	42	17	3	1	43	8	7	7	7	22	27	58
Ipswich	42	14	4	3	43	13	8	5	8	25	26	53
Arsenal	42	8	10	3	24	12	10	6	5	28	24	52
Nottm. Forest	42	16	4	1	44	11	4	4	13	19	32	48
Wolves	42	9	6	6	29	20	10	3	8	29	27	47

The "goals for" columns show the number of goals a team scored.
The "goals against" columns show the number of goals scored against a team.

1. Which team scored most goals?
2. Which team won most games?
3. Which team drew most games?

Goal difference is found by subtracting "goals against" from "goals for".
Liverpool scored 81 goals and had 30 scored against them. Their goal difference was 51.

4. Find the goal difference for each of the other teams.

During the season points were awarded to each team as follows:
   2 points for each match won
   1 point for each match drawn
   0 points for each match lost

5. What fraction of Nottm. Forest's points were won in away matches?
6. What percentage of Liverpool's points were won in home matches?

In 1981 the points system was changed.
Teams were awarded 3 points for a win instead of 2.
7. Calculate the number of points for each team with the new system.

Decimals

1. 4·8 × 5·3
2. 9·4 × 1·9
3. 2·4 × 5·5
4. 7·9 × 3·8
5. 16·5 × 4·7
6. 14·9 × 5·7
7. 23·7 × 8·4
8. 39·1 × 9·3
9. 4·79 × 3·6
10. 7·08 × 1·6
11. 5·24 × 2·8
12. 3·74 × 5·6
13. 12·97 × 5·2
14. 19·02 × 6·8
15. 3·78 × 1·8
16. 5·47 × 3·9

6·74 × 2·4

$$6 \cdot 74 \longleftarrow \text{2 decimal places}$$
$$\times \quad 2 \cdot 4 \longleftarrow \text{1 decimal place}$$
$$13480$$
$$+ 2696$$
$$16 \cdot 176 \longleftarrow \text{3 decimal places}$$

Look at the decimal places in the numbers being multiplied.
Look at the decimal places in the answer.
What do you notice?

17. 4·92 × 1·2
18. 24·7 × 0·45
19. 7·14 × 1·6
20. 24·6 × 1·5
21. 9·78 × 1·9
22. 36·78 × 4·3
23. 39·07 × 7·8
24. 1·34 × 9·7
25. 16·73 × 3·2
26. 1·3 × 0·79
27. 45·93 × 3·9
28. 0·347 × 19
29. 4·78 × 5·2
30. 76·74 × 7·8
31. 0·79 × 0·9
32. 16·92 × 4·7

Find the area of these shapes.

33.

2·7 m

4·2 m

34.

2·3 m

3·9 m

35.

3·15 m

4·7 m

36.

0·62 m

7·9 m

37.

3·8 m

5·94 m

38.

1·19 m

2·9 m

14

8 ÷ 4   Make each number 10 times greater.
         Is the answer the same?

15 ÷ 3   Make each number 10 times greater.
         Is the answer the same?

243 ÷ 9 Make each number 10 times greater.
         Is the answer the same?

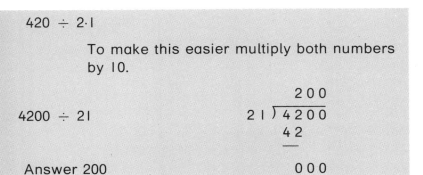

420 ÷ 2·1

> To make this easier multiply both numbers by 10.

4200 ÷ 21

```
          200
   21 ) 4 2 0 0
        4 2
        ──
        0 0 0
```

Answer 200

Do these in the same way.

1. 26 ÷ 1·3   2. 57 ÷ 1·9   3. 84 ÷ 2·1   4. 75 ÷ 2·5
5. 165 ÷ 3·3   6. 243 ÷ 2·7   7. 248 ÷ 3·1   8. 432 ÷ 7·2
9. 234 ÷ 1·3   10. 559 ÷ 4·3   11. 828 ÷ 3·6   12. 442 ÷ 1·7
13. 783 ÷ 8·7   14. 779 ÷ 1·9   15. 874 ÷ 2·3   16. 696 ÷ 2·4

Find the length of each rectangle.

17.

108 m²

1·8 m

18.

2·4 m   216 m²

19.

128 m²

1·6 m

Area

Calculate the areas of these shapes.

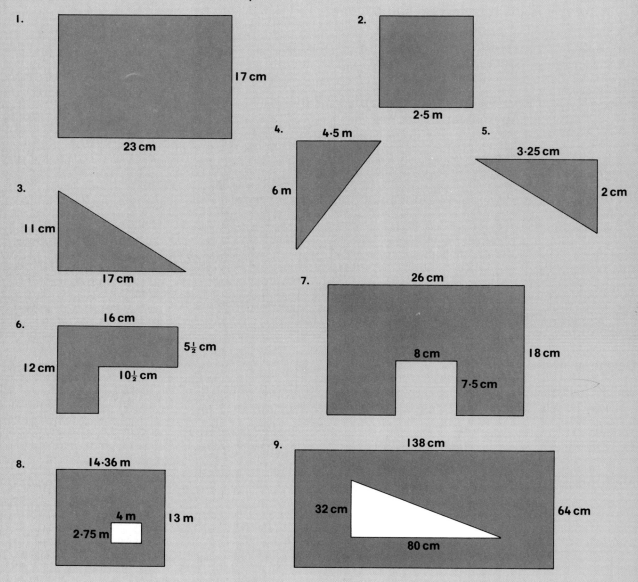

1. 17 cm, 23 cm

2. 2·5 m

4. 4·5 m, 6 m

5. 3·25 cm, 2 cm

3. 11 cm, 17 cm

7. 26 cm, 8 cm, 18 cm, 7·5 cm

6. 16 cm, 5½ cm, 12 cm, 10½ cm

8. 14·36 m, 4 m, 13 m, 2·75 m

9. 138 cm, 32 cm, 80 cm, 64 cm

10. Find the area of a room measuring 4·20 m by 3·50 m.
11. The area of a carpet is 4·2 m². The length is 2·1 m. What is the width?
12. What will be the cost of carpeting a room 3·25 m by 4 m with carpet costing £11·74 per m²?
13. The perimeter of a rug is 4·60 m, its length is 1·30 m. What is its area?
14. Calculate the perimeter of a square with an area of 144 m².
15. If the perimeter of a square was doubled, how many times larger would the area become?

Find the area of each shaded triangle in cm².
What fraction of the rectangle is it?

1.
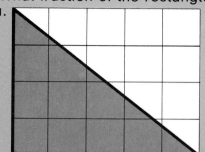

2.
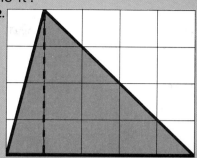

3.
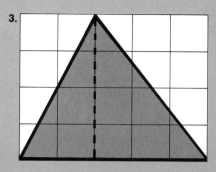

Find the areas of these triangles in cm².

4.
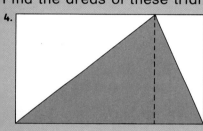

5.

6.
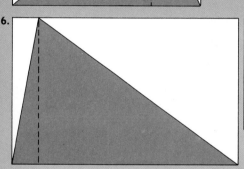

7.
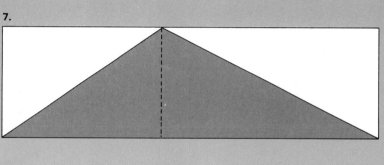

Area of a triangle $= \frac{1}{2}$ (base × height)

Calculate the areas of these triangles in cm².

8.
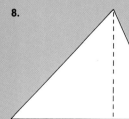

9.
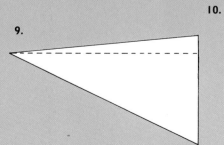

10.
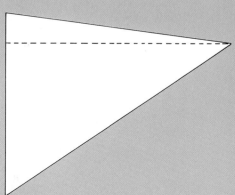

Fractions

1. $3\frac{1}{4} + 1\frac{1}{5}$

2. $5\frac{3}{8} + 1\frac{1}{3}$

3. $4\frac{5}{9} + 2\frac{5}{6}$

4. $\frac{7}{8} + 3\frac{1}{6}$

5. $2\frac{1}{2} + 3\frac{2}{3}$

6. $1\frac{5}{6} + 3\frac{3}{4}$

7. $3\frac{1}{2} + 2\frac{4}{7}$

8. $3\frac{5}{7} + 1\frac{2}{3}$

9. $6\frac{3}{4} - 2\frac{1}{3}$

10. $4\frac{1}{2} - \frac{2}{3}$

11. $2\frac{1}{6} - 1\frac{3}{4}$

12. $5\frac{3}{8} - 3\frac{3}{6}$

13. $6\frac{1}{2} - 2\frac{7}{11}$

14. $3\frac{2}{5} - 1\frac{2}{3}$

15. $7\frac{1}{5} - 2\frac{1}{4}$

16. $3\frac{3}{10} - 1\frac{3}{4}$

17. $1\frac{1}{4} \times 1\frac{1}{5}$

18. $1\frac{4}{7} \times 1\frac{5}{9}$

19. $3\frac{2}{3} \times 1\frac{4}{11}$

20. $2\frac{2}{5} \times 4\frac{3}{8}$

21. $3\frac{3}{4} \times 2\frac{2}{5}$

22. $4\frac{7}{8} \times 1\frac{3}{13}$

23. $1\frac{7}{9} \times 3\frac{3}{8}$

24. $4\frac{1}{5} \times 6\frac{2}{3}$

25. $\left(\frac{1}{4} + \frac{1}{2}\right) \times \frac{1}{3}$

26. $\frac{2}{3} + \left(\frac{1}{4} \times \frac{1}{2}\right)$

27. $\frac{1}{2} + \left(\frac{2}{3} \times \frac{1}{4}\right)$

28. $\frac{1}{4} - \left(\frac{1}{2} \times \frac{1}{3}\right)$

29. $\left(2\frac{2}{3} \times \frac{1}{4}\right) - \frac{5}{12}$

30. $\left(1\frac{3}{4} - \frac{3}{7}\right) \times \frac{2}{3}$

Find:

31. $\frac{2}{3}$ of 42

32. $\frac{7}{8}$ of 288 cm

33. $\frac{5}{6}$ of 114 g

34. $\frac{5}{9}$ of £108

35. $\frac{4}{5}$ of 95 kg

36. $\frac{4}{7}$ of 98 m

> Multiplying by a fraction is the same as dividing by its inverse.
>
> $63 \times \frac{1}{9}$ is the same as $63 \div 9$

37. $49 \times \frac{1}{7}$

38. $56 \times \frac{1}{8}$

39. $81 \times \frac{1}{9}$

40. $54 \times \frac{1}{6}$

41. $45 \times \frac{1}{9}$

42. $42 \times \frac{1}{3}$

43. $65 \times \frac{1}{5}$

44. $52 \times \frac{1}{4}$

45. $84 \times \frac{1}{4}$

46. $63 \times \frac{1}{7}$

47. $121 \times \frac{1}{11}$

48. $72 \times \frac{1}{9}$

49. $78 \times \frac{1}{6}$

50. $63 \times \frac{1}{3}$

51. $72 \times \frac{1}{6}$

52. $96 \times \frac{1}{8}$

Dividing by a fraction is the same as multiplying by its inverse.
$12 \div \frac{1}{4}$ is the same as 12×4

1. $12 \div \frac{1}{4}$

2. $8 \div \frac{1}{3}$

3. $7 \div \frac{1}{5}$

4. $4 \div \frac{1}{9}$

5. $6 \div \frac{1}{5}$

6. $14 \div \frac{1}{2}$

7. $11 \div \frac{1}{3}$

8. $3 \div \frac{1}{8}$

9. $9 \div \frac{1}{6}$

10. $7 \div \frac{1}{4}$

11. $12 \div \frac{1}{3}$

12. $4 \div \frac{1}{5}$

13. $15 \div \frac{1}{4}$

14. $6 \div \frac{1}{7}$

15. $8 \div \frac{1}{9}$

16. $13 \div \frac{1}{6}$

$$\frac{7}{8} \div \frac{3}{4}$$
$$= \frac{7}{\overset{}{\underset{2}{8}}} \times \frac{\overset{1}{\cancel{4}}}{3}$$
$$= \frac{7}{6}$$
$$= 1\frac{1}{6}$$

17. $\frac{3}{4} \div \frac{3}{8}$

18. $\frac{1}{2} \div \frac{3}{4}$

19. $\frac{2}{3} \div \frac{5}{6}$

20. $\frac{1}{2} \div \frac{3}{8}$

21. $\frac{1}{6} \div \frac{3}{4}$

22. $\frac{3}{5} \div \frac{9}{10}$

23. $\frac{4}{7} \div \frac{1}{14}$

24. $\frac{4}{9} \div \frac{2}{3}$

25. $\frac{7}{12} \div \frac{3}{4}$

26. $\frac{7}{8} \div \frac{1}{2}$

27. $\frac{7}{10} \div \frac{4}{5}$

28. $\frac{3}{5} \div \frac{7}{15}$

29. $\frac{5}{8} \div \frac{5}{12}$

30. $\frac{3}{4} \div \frac{5}{6}$

31. $\frac{2}{5} \div \frac{9}{10}$

32. $\frac{7}{8} \div \frac{7}{11}$

33. $\frac{3}{4} \div \frac{6}{7}$

34. $\frac{4}{9} \div \frac{8}{9}$

35. $\frac{3}{7} \div \frac{6}{11}$

36. $\frac{11}{12} \div \frac{1}{6}$

37. $\frac{7}{8} \div \frac{7}{12}$

38. $\frac{3}{5} \div \frac{2}{5}$

39. $\frac{7}{9} \div \frac{5}{6}$

40. $\frac{3}{4} \div \frac{9}{10}$

41. $\frac{4}{7} \div \frac{2}{7}$

42. $\frac{1}{2} \div \frac{9}{10}$

43. $\frac{5}{12} \div \frac{5}{16}$

44. $\frac{5}{8} \div \frac{9}{10}$

45. $\frac{7}{8} \div \frac{3}{4}$

46. $\frac{5}{6} \div \frac{5}{8}$

Graphs

Here are some facts and figures about a Sports Centre.
Draw the most suitable graphs to show the information given.

1.

People using the Centre on Tuesday morning			
Swimming	44	Bowls	11
Badminton	12	Skating	30
Squash	16	Table-tennis	10
Tennis	26	Netball	28

2.

People skating during one week			
Monday	180	Friday	200
Tuesday	135	Saturday	250
Wednesday	165	Sunday	225
Thursday	130		

3. It costs 45p to hire skates.
   Draw a ready reckoner graph to show the cost for up to 10 people.

This graph shows the approximate number of people who used the Sports Centre during one week.

The symbol 👤 represents 100 people.

Monday	👤 👤 👤 👤 👤
Tuesday	👤 👤 👤 👤 👤 👤 👤
Wednesday	👤 👤 👤 👤 👤 👤 👤 👤
Thursday	👤 👤 👤 👤 👤 👤 👤 👤
Friday	👤 👤 👤 👤 👤 👤 👤 👤
Saturday	👤 👤 👤 👤 👤 👤 👤 👤 👤 👤
Sunday	👤 👤 👤 👤 👤 👤 👤 👤 👤

1. On which day did the most people attend the Centre?

2. On which day did the fewest people attend the Centre?

3. How many people attended the Centre on Thursday?

4. How many people attended the Centre on Friday?

5. On which days did 800 people attend the Centre?

6. This table shows the number of people who played squash each day.

Day	Mon	Tues	Wed	Thur	Fri	Sat	Sun
Number	40	35	35	60	60	70	85

Use the symbol 👤 to represent 10 people.

Draw a graph to show this information.

Number

$$13 \times 12 = \boxed{156}$$
$$12 \times 13 = \boxed{156}$$
$$156 \div 12 = \boxed{13}$$
$$156 \div 13 = \boxed{12}$$

Look at these examples.
If you are told the answer to one of them, you can easily find the answers to the others.

Work these out in the same way.
Use the example you are given to complete the others.

1.
$$16 \times 11 = 176$$
So $11 \times 16 = \boxed{}$
$$176 \div 11 = \boxed{}$$
$$176 \div 16 = \boxed{}$$

2.
$$14 \times 15 = 210$$
So $15 \times 14 = \boxed{}$
$$210 \div 14 = \boxed{}$$
$$210 \div 15 = \boxed{}$$

3.
$$204 \div 12 = 17$$
So $204 \div 17 = \boxed{}$
$$17 \times 12 = \boxed{}$$
$$12 \times 17 = \boxed{}$$

Find an easy way to do these:

4.
$$236 \times 8 = 1888$$
So $236 \times 16 = \boxed{}$
$$236 \times 4 = \boxed{}$$

5.
$$748 + 629 = 1377$$
So $748 + 1629 = \boxed{}$
$$1748 + 629 = \boxed{}$$

6.
$$1000 \div 5 = 200$$
So $2000 \div 5 = \boxed{}$
$$3000 \div 5 = \boxed{}$$

7.
$$150 \times 10 = 1500$$
So $150 \times 5 = \boxed{}$
$$150 \times 20 = \boxed{}$$

8.
$$2164 - 872 = 1292$$
So $2164 - 1872 = \boxed{}$
$$3164 - 872 = \boxed{}$$

9.
$$726 + 198 = 924$$
So $1726 + 198 = \boxed{}$
$$1726 + 1198 = \boxed{}$$

10.
$$450 \div 6 = 75$$
So $450 \div 3 = \boxed{}$
$$900 \div 6 = \boxed{}$$

11.
$$3006 - 192 = 2814$$
So $3006 - 1192 = \boxed{}$
$$4006 - 192 = \boxed{}$$

12.
$$4213 - 870 = 3343$$
So $4213 - 1870 = \boxed{}$
$$5213 - 1870 = \boxed{}$$

Percentages

Find:

1. 8% of £50
2. 48% of £25
3. 60% of £35
4. 90% of 60 l
5. 65% of 40 kg
6. 24% of 25 m
7. 30% of 70 kg
8. 48% of 50 l
9. 12% of 75 m
10. 80% of 45 l
11. 36% of £25
12. 15% of 40 kg

Write as a percentage:

13. 48 out of 75
14. 16 out of 64
15. 24 out of 40
16. 56 out of 70
17. 81 out of 90
18. 32 out of 80
19. 36 out of 45
20. 14 out of 70
21. 17 out of 68
22. 18 out of 72
23. 21 out of 35
24. 52 out of 65

25. Coal costing £6 is reduced by 30% for the summer months. What is its new price?

26. In a 120 kg load of coal there is 5% coal dust. What is the weight of the coal dust?

27. For each 120 tonnes of coal mined, 96 tonnes are of the best quality coal. What percentage is this?

28. For each 75 tonnes mined, 63 tonnes of coal are sold to industry. The remainder is sold to the public. What percentage is sold to the public?

29. A factory spends £6200 a week on fuel. Gas takes 14% of this, 48% is coal and the remainder is electricity. Calculate how much is spent on the three types of fuel.

Measurement

Measure the circumference and
diameter of a cylinder in mm.
Record your results.

How many times does the diameter
divide into the circumference?

What must the diameter be multiplied
by to find the circumference?

Do the same with other cylinders.
Record your results.
Tell your teacher what you notice.

Measure the diameter of each circle.
Calculate each circumference.

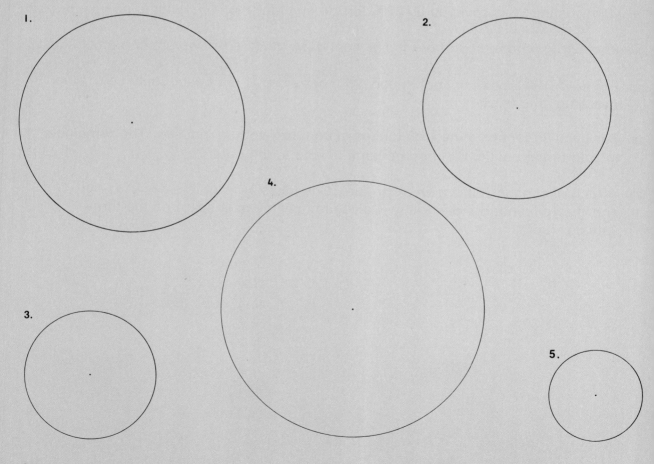

1.

2.

4.

3.

5.

24

The circumference of a circle is 3·14 times greater than its diameter.

> Circumference = 3·14 × diameter
> Circumference = 3·14 × d

The Greeks used their letter pi (π) to show 3·14

> Circumference = π × d

Calculate the circumference of these circles.

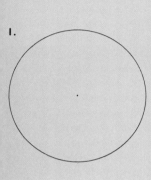

1.

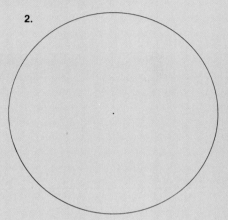

2.

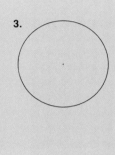

3.

Calculate the circumference of circles with these diameters.

4. 4 m   5. 26 mm   6. 31 cm   7. 22 m   8. 5·5 cm

Calculate the circumference of circles with these radii.

9. 3 m   10. 6 cm   11. 19 mm   12. 4·5 cm   13. 1·25 m

Which of these shapes has the greater perimeter?

14.

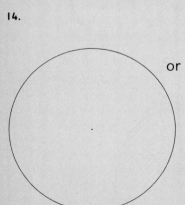 or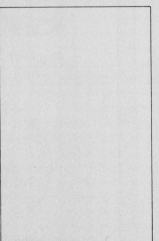

15.

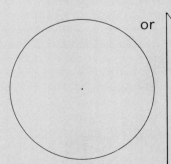 or

Trundle wheel

Remember circumference = π × diameter

circumference = π × d

I. Measure the diameter of a trundle wheel.
   Calculate its circumference.
   What do you notice?

The distance travelled in one revolution of a wheel is its circumference.

Calculate how far each of these cycles will move in one revolution of the front wheel.

2.

Diameter of front wheel = 63 cm

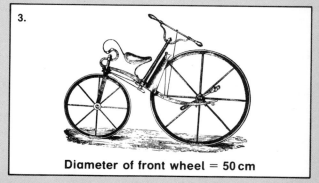

3.

Diameter of front wheel = 50 cm

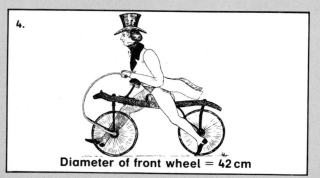

4.

Diameter of front wheel = 42 cm

5.

Diameter of front wheel = 105 cm

Area

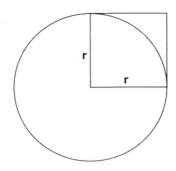

The area of a circle $\backsimeq$ 3 × area of the square on the radius.

The area of the square is r × r; this is written as r^2.

So the approximate area of a circle is 3 × r^2.

1. Calculate the approximate area of the circle at the top of the page.

The area of a circle can be calculated more accurately.

Area of a circle = 3·14 × r^2

We write 3·14 as π

Area = π × r^2

2. Calculate the area of the circle at the top of the page.

Calculate the area of circles with these radii.
3. 4 cm   4. 7 cm   5. 11 mm   6. 20 cm   7. 15 m

Which of these shapes has the greater area?
8.   9.

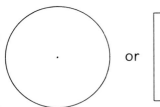 or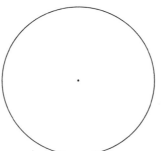

Relationships

Here is a family tree.

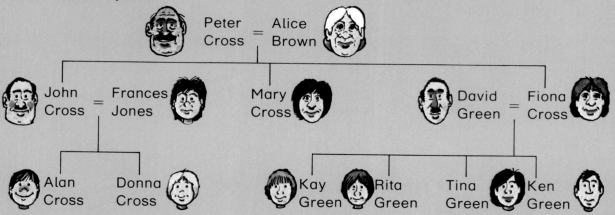

1. How many children have David and Fiona Green?
2. How many grandchildren have Peter and Alice Cross?
3. Who is Alan Cross's uncle?
4. Who are the aunts of Tina Green?
5. What is Frances Jones' married name?
6. What relation is Alan Cross to Kay Green?
7. What relation is Rita Green to Ken Green?
8. What relation is Donna Cross to Alice Cross?

Arrows can be drawn to show relationships.

The arrows show the relationship **is the husband of**.

The arrows have been reversed.

9. Write the relationship shown by these arrows.
The **direction of the arrow** is very important.

1. Draw arrows to show the relationship **is the father of**.

Peter

John   Frances   Mary

Alan   Donna

2. Draw arrows to show the relationship **is the son of**.

Alice

John   David

Alan   Rita   Ken

John   Frances   Mary   Fiona   David   ⟶ means **is the sister of**.

Why have Mary and Fiona been joined with ⟷ ?

3. Draw arrows to show the relationship **is the sister of**.

Kay   Rita   Tina   Ken

4. Write the relationship shown by these arrows.

Peter   Alice

John   Frances   Mary   Fiona   David

Donna   Rita

Now join other people who have this relationship.

5. Write the relationship shown by this arrow.

Alan   Donna

Kay   Rita   Tina   Ken

Now join other people who have this relationship.

Number

Remember that the direction of the arrow is important.
Complete each set of numbers.

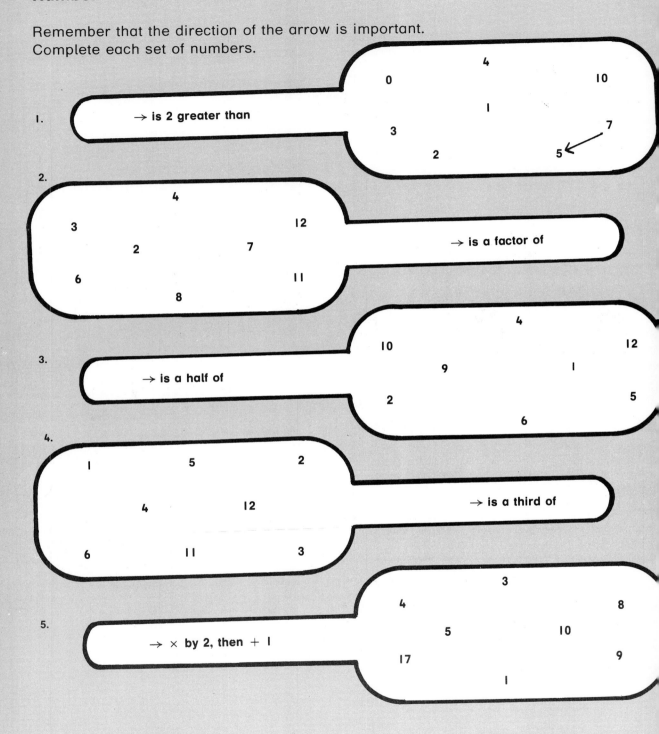

1. → is 2 greater than

0   4   10

1

3

2   5   7

2. → is a factor of

4

3   12

2   7

6   11

8

3. → is a half of

4

10   12

9   1

2   5

6

4. → is a third of

1   5   2

4   12

6   11   3

5. → × by 2, then + 1

3

4   8

5   10

17   9

1

6. If the direction of each arrow in questions 1 to 5 is reversed, what will each relationship be?

30

Follow the instructions on this flow diagram.

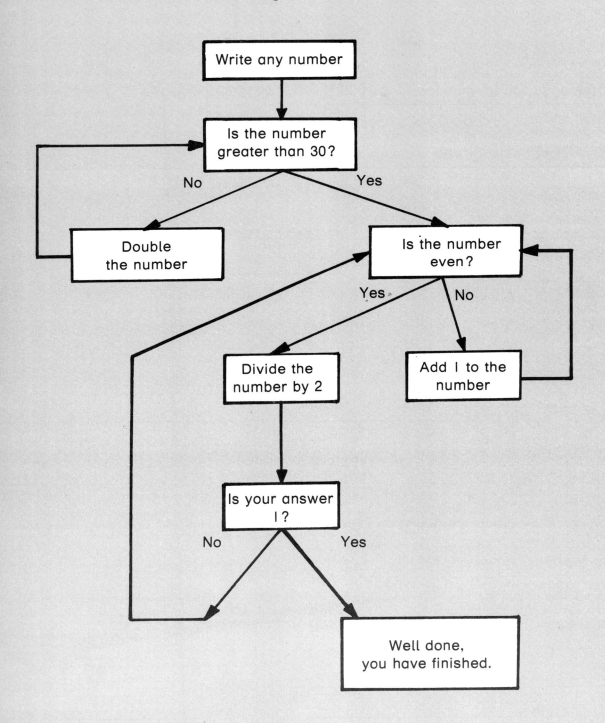

Begin with a different number.

Graphs

This large milk tanker holds 15 thousand litres of milk.
It empties its milk into a cooling machine.
It takes 1 hour 40 minutes to empty the tanker.
This table shows how much milk is left in the tanker at
intervals of 20 minutes.

Time emptying (in minutes)	0	20	40	60	80	100
Milk left (in thousand litres)	15	8	3·5	1·5	0·5	0

The information is plotted on this graph.

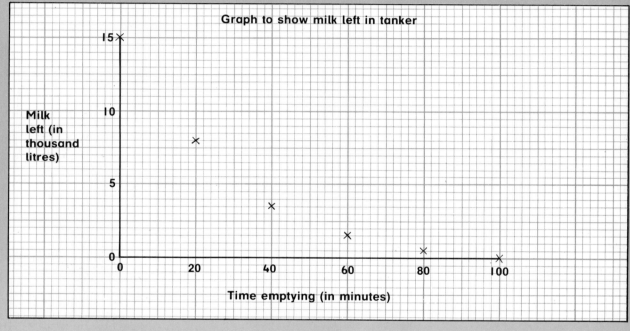

Graph to show milk left in tanker

Copy the graph.
The points on the graph are in a curve.

They can be joined up like this:

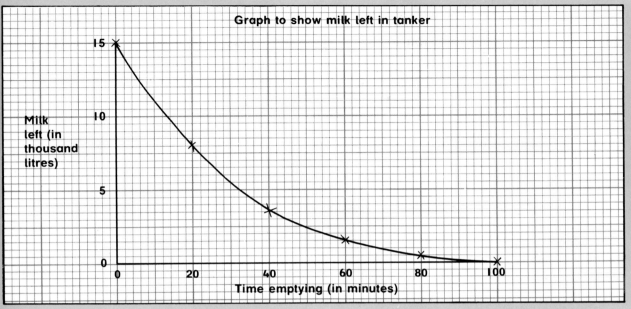

Graph to show milk left in tanker

Join them up on your graph in the same way. You have drawn a **curved line graph**.

From the graph find out how much milk is left in the tanker after

1. 70 minutes.   2. 10 minutes.

A smaller milk tanker holds 10 thousand litres of milk.
It only takes 50 minutes to empty.
This table shows how much milk is left in the tanker at intervals of 10 minutes.

Time emptying (in minutes)	0	10	20	30	40	50
Milk left (in thousand litres)	10	6	3	1·5	0·5	0

Draw a curved line graph to show this information.

Number

Complete these number patterns.

1. 2   3   5   7   11   *   *   *   23
2. 1   3   6   10   15   *   *   *   45
3. 1   4   9   16   25   *   *   *   81

The three patterns show square numbers, prime numbers and triangular numbers. Can you write which pattern is which?

Let us look more closely at square numbers.

We know that $3 \times 3 = 9$

We say that 3 squared equals 9

We can write this as $3^2 = 9$

4 squared equals 16

$4^2 = 16$

Write the value of these:

4. 5^2 5. 7^2 6. 9^2

7. 10^2 8. 14^2 9. 22^2

We know that $36 = 6 \times 6$

We say that the **square root** of 36 equals 6

We write this as $\sqrt{36} = 6$

The square root of 81 equals 9

$\sqrt{81} = 9$

Write the value of these:

10. $\sqrt{16}$ 11. $\sqrt{100}$ 12. $\sqrt{64}$

13. $\sqrt{49}$ 14. $\sqrt{144}$

Let us look at some mathematical shorthand.

We know that $4 \times 4 = 4^2$

So $4 \times 4 \times 4 = 4^3$

And $6 \times 6 \times 6 \times 6 = 6^4$

Write these in the shorthand way.

1. $2 \times 2 \times 2 \times 2 \times 2$ 2. $3 \times 3 \times 3 \times 3 \times 3 \times 3$ 3. $7 \times 7 \times 7$

4. $8 \times 8 \times 8 \times 8$ 5. $10 \times 10 \times 10$ 6. $4 \times 4 \times 4 \times 4 \times 4$

7. $5 \times 5 \times 5 \times 5 \times 5$ 8. $6 \times 6 \times 6 \times 6$ 9. $10 \times 10 \times 10 \times 10 \times 10$

Write these in full.

10. 4^4 11. 3^2 12. 10^4

13. 8^5 14. 2^6 15. 6^3

$2^4 = 2 \times 2 \times 2 \times 2$ $3^3 = 3 \times 3 \times 3$

$\quad = 16$ $\quad\quad = 27$

Write the value of these.

16. 4^2 17. 4^3 18. 10^4

19. 5^3 20. 2^5 21. 8^4

If $a = 2$ $b = 5$ $c = 12$, what are the value of these:

22. a^6 23. b^2 24. c^2

25. a^3 26. b^4 27. c^3

Write the value of these.

28. 13^2 29. 15^2 30. 19^2

31. 25^2 32. 36^2 33. 47^2

Choose the correct answer.

34. $196 = \begin{bmatrix} 14^2 \\ 16^2 \\ 24^2 \end{bmatrix}$ 35. $512 = \begin{bmatrix} 7^3 \\ 8^3 \\ 9^3 \end{bmatrix}$ 36. $2187 = \begin{bmatrix} 3^7 \\ 3^6 \\ 3^5 \end{bmatrix}$

Shape

Draw a triangle in your book.
Mark a point 0 about 3 cm from the triangle.

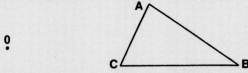

Now draw straight lines from 0 to pass through each vertex of the triangle.
Extend each line well past the triangle.

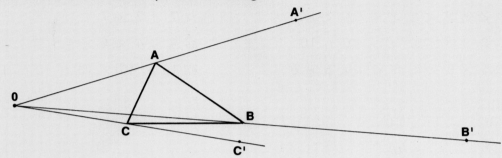

Make marks so that:

0A' is double 0A.

0B' is double 0B.

0C' is double 0C.

Join A' B' C'.

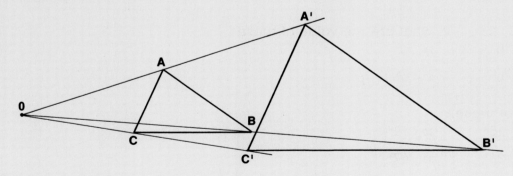

The shape has been enlarged.
Now draw another shape so that:

0A' is treble 0A.

0B' is treble 0B.

0C' is treble 0C.

Choose some shapes of your own and enlarge them.

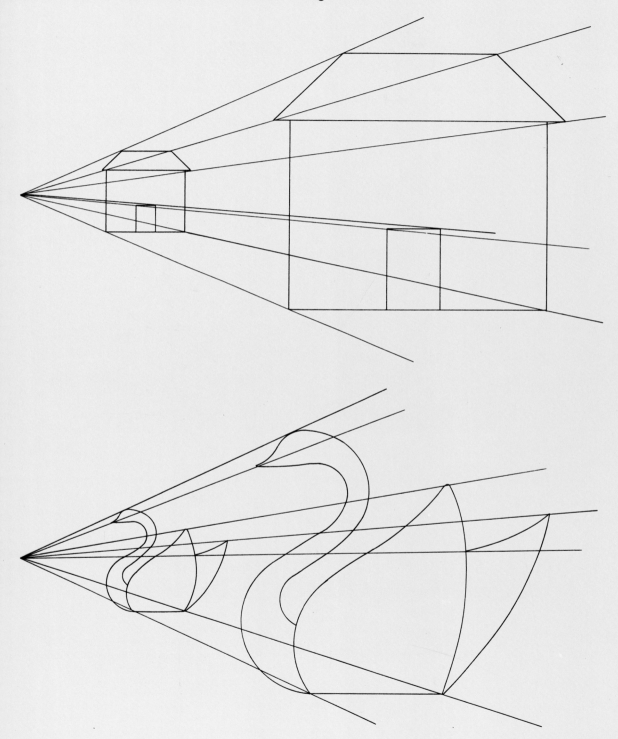

Number

Underline the digit which is worth the most in each of these.

1. 436
2. 0·245
3. 5·36
4. 1741
5. 28·9

6. £374·20
7. 3·782 kg
8. 4177 m
9. 37·5 l
10. 3674 mm

Write these numbers to the nearest 100
{
11. 364
12. 5234
13. 36421
14. 27568
}

to the nearest 1000
{
15. 4754
16. 6194
17. 17424
18. 29870
}

Remember: ≏ means **is approximately equal to**

4·740 kg ≏ 5 kg

Approximate these to the nearest whole unit.

19. £3·74
20. 4·098 kg
21. 3·670 l
22. 73·478 km

23. 3·47 m
24. £23·08
25. 5·506 kg
26. £436·40

Choose the correct answer to each of these by approximating.

27. $3·4 \times 2·78 =$
{
9·452
94·52
945·2
}

28. $4·5^2 =$
{
2·025
20·25
202·5
}

29. $6·36 \div 12 =$
{
5·3
53
0·53
}

30. $\sqrt{225} =$
{
15
150
1·5
}

Complete with the correct symbol > < or =

31. 4·0 ☐ 4
32. 0·003 ☐ 0·3
33. 800·0 ☐ 8000

34. 0·500 ☐ 0·5
35. 0·60 ☐ 0·06
36. 0·02 ☐ 0·20

1. $6293 + 728 + 1069$

2. $57 + 3213 + 189$

3. $4306 - 1927$

4. $1006 - 843$

5. $1628 + 2392 - 1079$

6. $4316 - 1997 + 1023$

7. 4013×4

8. 997×18

9. $1625 \div 5$

10. $4384 \div 8$

11. $15\cdot3 \div 1\cdot7$

12. $408 \div 2\cdot4$

13. By what amount is £12·70 greater than £9·85?

14. Find the total weight of 1·5 kg, 275 g and 1·460 kg.

15. What is the total capacity of 8 containers each holding 4·75 l?

16. What is the average of £7·24, £0·52, £6·95, and £5·01?

17. What is the difference between $2\frac{1}{2}$ kg and 795 g?

18. How much more is 8·75 l than 2520 ml?

19. Add together 2·6, 1·75 and 2·385.

20. From 6·24 subtract 3·9.

21. Three sums of money add up to £100.
    The largest amount is £48·30.
    The smallest amount is £6·50.
    What is the other amount?

22. The average weight of 6 crates is 181·5 kg.
    What is their total weight?

23. A man and his son weigh 108 kg.
    The man weighs twice as much as his son.
    How much do they each weigh?

24. The total of three numbers is 4921.
    Two of the numbers are the same.
    The other number is 1965.
    What are the three numbers?

25. $\frac{2}{3}$ of a sum of money is £26·28.
    What is $\frac{1}{3}$ of the sum of money?
    What is the sum of money?

We round off numbers for many reasons.

When it is difficult to record a measurement exactly.

To remember numbers more easily.

When an exact answer would be silly or is not needed.

When rounding off a number, the most important digits are those which are worth the most. These digits are called the **significant figures**.

£8184   rounded off to 1 significant figure is £8000

rounded off to 2 significant figures is £8200

Round these numbers off to 1 significant figure.

1. The cost of a Thompsons Holiday is £4021.

2. The population of New York is 7 895 000.

Round these numbers off to 2 significant figures.

1. The weight of the luggage
   is 53·26 kg.

2. The aeroplane flew 249
   passengers to New York.

3. It is 6075 km to New York.

4. The aeroplane flies at 3235 m high.

These questions have been answered exactly.
Write each answer as a sensible approximation.
For each answer write how many significant figures you have used.

5. A stetson costs 21·34 dollars.

6. There were 4037 people at the rodeo.

7. The Empire State building is
   448·6 m high.

8. We travelled 8946 km during
   the holiday.

Shape

Calculate the areas of these triangles.

1.

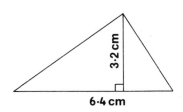

3·2 cm

6·4 cm

2.

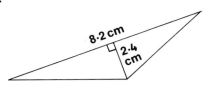

8·2 cm

2·4 cm

3.

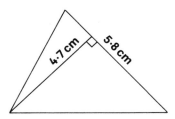

4·7 cm 5·8 cm

4.

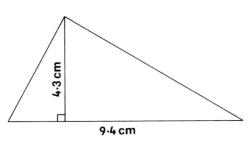

4·3 cm

9·4 cm

Remember: The angles of a triangle add up to 180°

Calculate the third angle.

5.

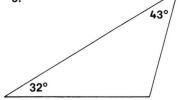

43°

32°

6.

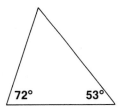

72°   53°

7.

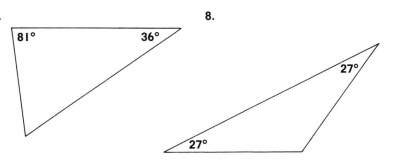

81°   36°

8.

27°

27°

9.

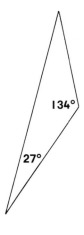

134°

27°

42

Protractor

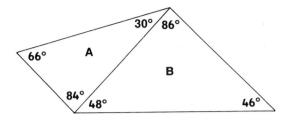

Triangles A and B are joined together to make a quadrilateral.
The angles of triangle A add up to 180°.
The angles of triangle B add up to 180°.
The angles of the quadrilateral add up to 360°.

1. Measure the angles of this quadrilateral.

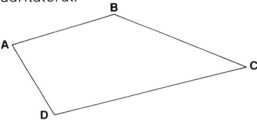

Record each angle and find the total.

The angles of a quadrilateral add up to 360°

Calculate the unknown angle.

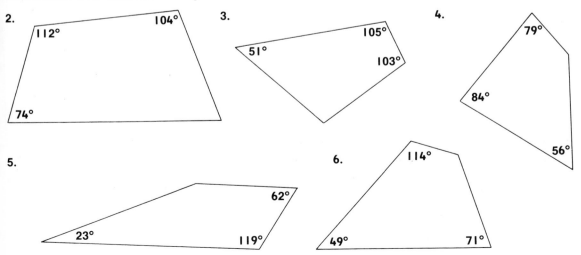

Graphs

1. Complete this table of square numbers.

Number to be squared	0	1	2	3	4	5	6	7	8	9	10
Square number	0	1	4	9							

2. Draw these axes.

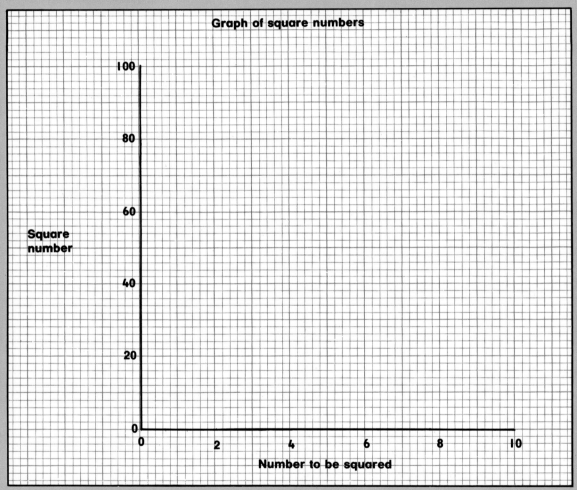

Plot the square numbers on the graph.

Join the points up to make a curved line graph.

From the graph find the approximate answers to:

3. $1 \cdot 6^2$ 4. $3 \cdot 4^2$ 5. $7 \cdot 2^2$ 6. $4 \cdot 4^2$ 7. $6 \cdot 5^2$

Check your answers with a calculator.

Mr. Chilcott bought a car for £4000.
The graph shows how its value dropped each year for six years.

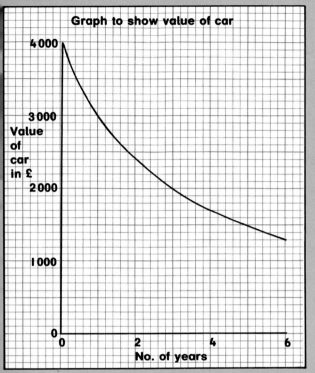

1. Compile a table showing its value each year.
2. Work out how much it loses in value each year.
3. How much do you think it will be worth after seven years?

This graph shows the number of people hurt in road accidents in a year.

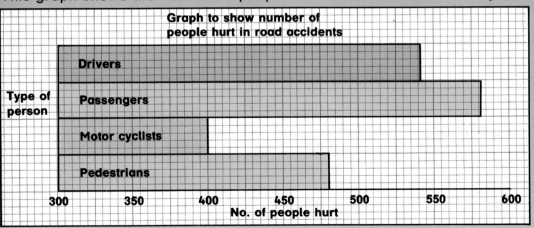

4. How many of each type of person was hurt?
5. How many people were hurt altogether?
6. What percentage of the people hurt were motor cyclists?
7. 15% of those hurt were children. How many children were hurt?

45

Algebra

Find the missing number.

1. $16 + \square = 24$

2. $19 - \square = 3$

3. $\square - 12 = 4$

4. $6 \times \square = 42$

5. $\square \times 9 = 63$

6. $4 \times 8 = \square$

7. $54 \div \square = 6$

8. $56 \div 7 = \square$

9. $\square \div 6 = 5$

10. $\dfrac{\square}{7} = 6$

11. $\dfrac{32}{4} = \square$

12. $\dfrac{81}{\square} = 9$

Find the value of the letter.

13. $16 + a = 37$

14. $y - 9 = 15$

15. $17 + 30 = c$

16. $7 \times a = 35$

17. $x \times 3 = 24$

18. $6 \times 9 = g$

19. $36 \div t = 6$

20. $72 \div 8 = y$

21. $m \div 5 = 9$

22. $\dfrac{36}{p} = 9$

23. $\dfrac{48}{6} = x$

24. $\dfrac{b}{8} = 5$

$7 \times a$ can be written $7a$

$3 \times x$ can be written $3x$

Find the value of the letter.

25. $2x = 12$

26. $6y = 42$

27. $8a = 72$

28. $4m = 28$

29. $5p = 40$

30. $7q = 35$

31. $3a = 36$

32. $9b = 81$

33. $6c = 54$

34. $6n = 72$

35. $8d = 48$

36. $9s = 72$

If $k = 6$, $r = 20$, $s = 4$ and $x = 3$ what are the values of these:

37. $2s + 4$

38. $x + 3s$

39. $9 + 3k$

40. $3x + 2s$

41. $r - 2x$

42. $4k - r$

43. $x + 3s - k$

44. $4s - 4x$

45. $kx + r$

46. $\dfrac{ks}{4}$

47. $\dfrac{sx}{k}$

48. $\dfrac{r}{5} + k$

46

Number

$1\frac{1}{2}$ million written in full is 1 500 000.
£3·1 million written in full is £3 100 000.
Write each of the following numbers in full.

1.
> $2\frac{1}{4}$ million unemployed

2.
> Firm wins order for £2·4 million

3.
> $\frac{3}{4}$ million tourists visit National Park

4.
> Car firm loses £1·6 million order

5.
> Sales of Tanda bicycles top 3·2 million in first year

In these examples use numbers less than 30.

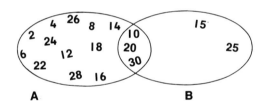

Circle A contains even numbers.
Circle B contains multiples of 5.
Some numbers are both.
These have been written in the intersection.

Now do these in the same way.

6.
A – prime numbers
B – odd numbers

7.
A – square numbers
B – multiples of 3

8.
A – factors of 24
B – factors of 21

9.
A – multiples of 6
B – factors of 30

47

Percentages

Mr. Atkins bought a car. To take it on the road he had to insure it. As Mr. Atkins had never had an accident he received a discount from the insurance company called a "no-claim bonus".

1. How much did Mr. Atkins pay each year to insure his car?

Alsure Insurance Company			
	Insurance premium	Discount	Cost
1st year	£280	no discount	
2nd year	£320	40%	
3rd year	£360	50%	
4th year	£420	55%	
5th year	£450	60%	

Mr. Atkins had other car costs.
His car used one litre of petrol every 10 km.
Each litre of petrol cost 50p.
Mr. Atkins travelled 16 000 km in a year.

2. What were his petrol costs in that year?

While owning the car, Mr. Atkins had three repair bills. One for £120, one for £85 and one for £190.
The garage gave 5% discount on all bills, if they were paid promptly.

3. Mr. Atkins paid the bills promptly. How much did he have to pay the garage?

Graphs

Halfpenny Bridge is a toll bridge.
5600 vehicles passed over it last week.
This pie chart shows how many of each type crossed the bridge.

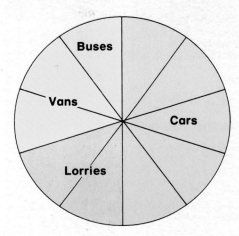

1. How many of each type of vehicle used the bridge?
2. What percentage of the vehicles were lorries?
3. What percentage of the vehicles were buses?

1840 pedestrians walked across the bridge.
This pie chart shows how many were adults and how many were children.

4. How many adults crossed the bridge?
5. How many children crossed the bridge?
6. What percentage of the pedestrians were women?
7. What percentage of the pedestrians were men?
8. What percentage of the pedestrians were children?

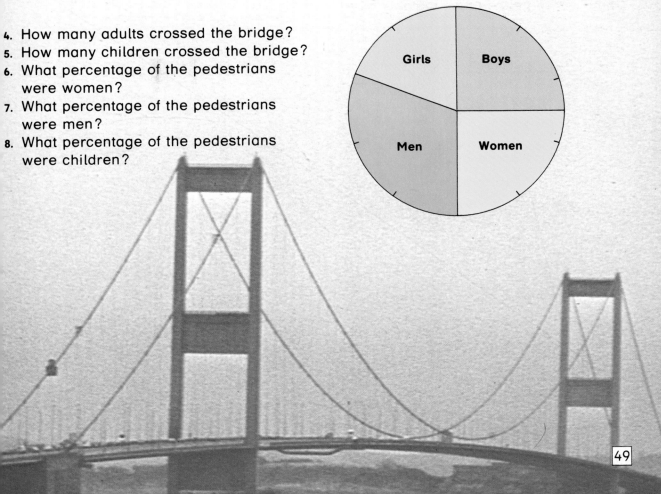

Algebra

$$\triangle = \square + 2$$

If $\square$ is worth 1

then $\triangle$ is worth 3

$$\boxed{3} = \boxed{1} + 2$$

1. $\triangle = \square + 4$

What is the value of $\triangle$ if

$\square$ = 0, 2, 3, 5, 7?

2. $\triangle = \square - 2$

What is the value of $\triangle$ if

$\square$ = 2, 3, 4, 5, 7?

3. $\triangle = \square + 1$

What is the value of $\square$ if

$\triangle$ = 2, 3, 4, 6, 8?

4. $\triangle = \square - 1$

What is the value of $\square$ if

$\triangle$ = 0, 1, 2, 3, 4?

Copy and complete these tables.

5. $\triangle = \square + 2$

$\square$	0	1	2	3	4
$\triangle$					

6. $\triangle = \square - 1$

$\square$	1	2	3	4	6
$\triangle$					

7. $\triangle = \square + 3$

$\triangle$	3	4	5	6	8
$\square$					

8. $\triangle = \square - 2$

$\triangle$	2	3	4	5	6
$\square$					

9. $\triangle = \square + 5$

$\triangle$	5		6	8	
$\square$		2			4

10. $\triangle = \square - 3$

$\triangle$			5	3	6
$\square$	4			5	

11. $\triangle = \square + 6$

$\triangle$	6			11	13
$\square$		2	4		

12. $\triangle = \square - 4$

$\triangle$	0		2	3	
$\square$		5			9

△ = ☐ + 2

△	2	3	4	5	6
☐	0	1	2	3	4

The information in the table can
be drawn on a graph.

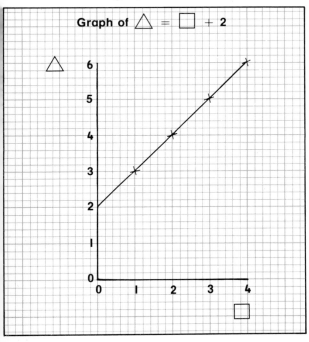

Graph of △ = ☐ + 2

Draw graphs to show:

1. △ = ☐ + 1

△	1	2	3	4	5
☐	0	1	2	3	4

2. △ = ☐ + 3

△	3	4	5	6	7
☐	0	1	2	3	4

3. △ = ☐ − 2

△	0	1	2	3	4
☐	2	3	4	5	6

4. △ = ☐ − 1

△	0	1	2	3	4
☐					

5. △ = ☐ − 3

△	0	1	2	3	4
☐					

6. △ = ☐ + 4

△					
☐	0	1	2	3	4

51

Christine plays in her school band.
A picture of the band is on the opposite page.
This list shows the cost of the instruments they use.

Rhythm instruments	Melody instruments
Drum £23·00 each	Xylophone £74·75 each
Tambour £7·00 each	Descant recorders £2·50 each
Cymbals £4·75 a pair	Treble recorders £6·50 each
Tambourine £7·50 each	
Bells £2·00 a set	

1. What was the total cost of the rhythm instruments?

2. What was the total cost of the melody instruments?

3. How much did it cost to buy all the instruments?

4. What fraction of the total cost were the tambourines?

5. What percentage of the total cost were the descant recorders?

The band gave a concert to parents.
The price of admission tickets was 50p for adults, 30p for children.
225 adults and 75 children attended the concert.

6. How much money was made from the sale of tickets?

7. What fraction of the audience were children?

8. What was the ratio of adults to children in the audience?

If you had £250 to buy instruments for a school band, what would you buy? Your list of instruments should cost approximately £250.

Shape

Compasses, set square, protractor

Construct these shapes.
Measure the length of x in each shape you have drawn.

1.

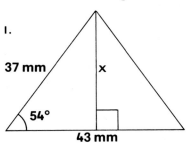

37 mm

x

54°

43 mm

2.

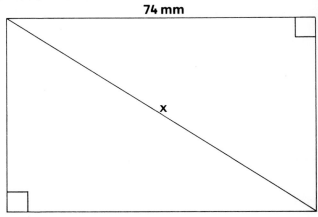

74 mm

48 mm

x

3.

135°   135°

x

36 mm

50 mm

4.

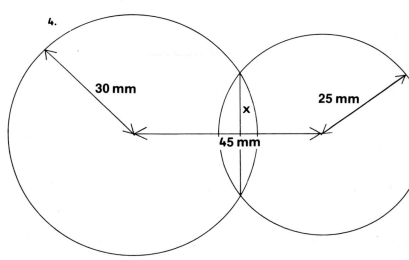

30 mm

25 mm

x

45 mm

5.

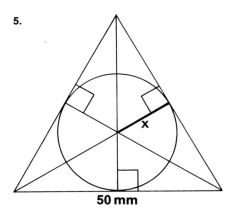

x

50 mm

6.

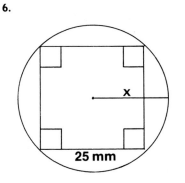

x

25 mm

360° protractor

Use your 360° protractor to measure this angle.
Tell your teacher the answer.

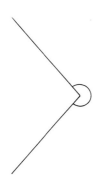

An angle greater than 180° is called a **reflex angle**

Measure these reflex angles.

I.   **2.**   **3.**

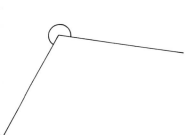
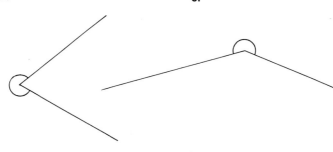

Draw angles measuring:

4. 190°   **5.** 275°   **6.** 245°   **7.** 335°

Measure the reflex angle in each quadrilateral.

8.   **9.**

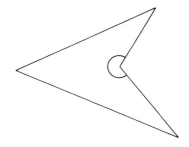
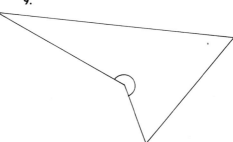

Measurement

Sometimes it is necessary to measure direction very accurately. This compass shows degrees.

The direction of Baslow on the compass is 45°.

We say the **bearing** of Baslow is 045°.

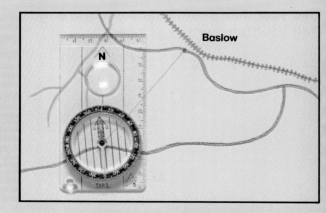

ı. Write the bearing of each town.

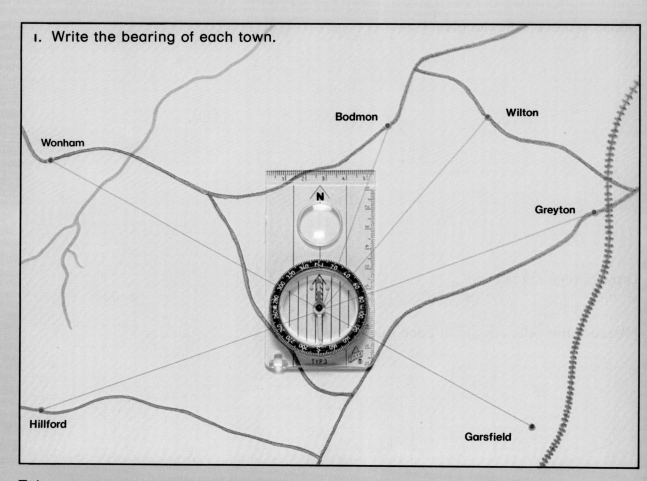

Take your compass into the playground and find the bearings of four different objects in the distance.

Shape

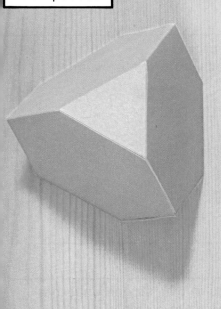

This is a truncated tetrahedron.
Construct the net below to make your own.

Measurement

A4 sized paper, cardboard, weights

Draw a 10 mm margin.

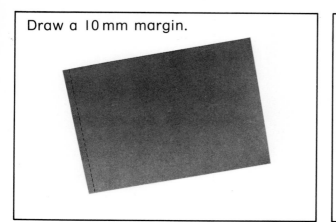

Glue the margin.
Fold the paper to make a cylinder.

Put a 100 mm square of cardboard on the cylinder.

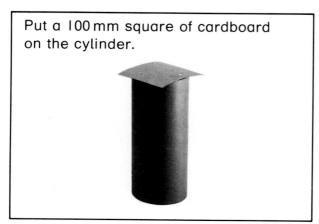

Add weights in 50 g stages until the cylinder begins to collapse.
Record the weight at which the cylinder collapsed.

Make prisms with A4 paper. Allow a 10 mm margin for gluing.
Do the same as before, adding weights in 50 g stages.
Record the weight at which each prism collapsed.

Which prism held the greatest weight?

Imperial units

The Imperial units of Length are miles, yards (yds), feet (ft), and inches (ins).

    12 ins = 1 ft
     3 ft   = 1 yd
    1760 yds = 1 mile

1. Find out how many cm are approximately equal to 1 ft.
2. Calculate how many cm are approximately equal to 1 yd.
   Find out whether your answer is correct.

The Imperial units of Weight are tons, hundredweight (cwt), stones (st), pounds (lb) and ounces (ozs).

    16 ozs = 1 lb
    14 lb = 1 st
     8 st = 1 cwt
    20 cwt = 1 ton

3. Find out how many g are approximately equal to 1 oz.
4. Calculate how many g weigh approximately the same as 1 lb.
   Find out whether your answer is correct.

The Imperial units of Capacity are gallons (gall) and pints (pts).

    8 pts = 1 gall

One gallon is approximately the same as 4·5 litres.

    1 gall ≈ 4·5 l

5. Draw a graph showing the conversion of gallons to litres.
6. Use the graph to convert the following to litres:

    5 gall, 8 gall, 10 gall, 6·5 gall, 3·5 gall, 2·75 gall.

Shape

Compasses, a piece of string, drawing pins

Cut out a paper circle, radius 5 cm.
Mark a point A.
Fold any part of the circumference
to touch A.

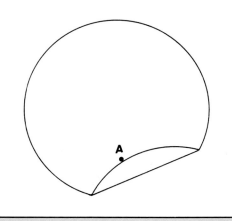

Make as many different folds of the
circumference to touch A as you can.
Your circle should look like this:

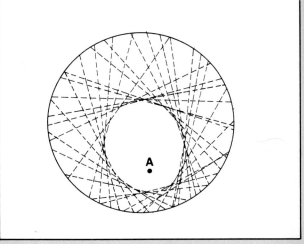

Place a sheet of paper on a wooden board.
Press two drawing pins into the board about 14 cm apart.
Find a length of string about 30 cm long and tie it into a loop.
Draw a shape like this.

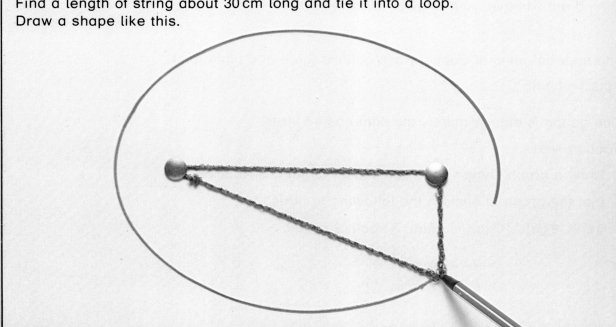

The shapes you have drawn are called **ellipses**.
Here is another way of drawing an ellipse.

Draw a line 120 mm long.
Mark off each 10 mm.
From the middle point draw a circle of radius 30 mm.

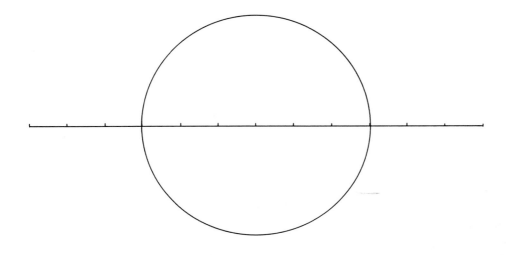

Use the diagram below to help you to draw an ellipse.

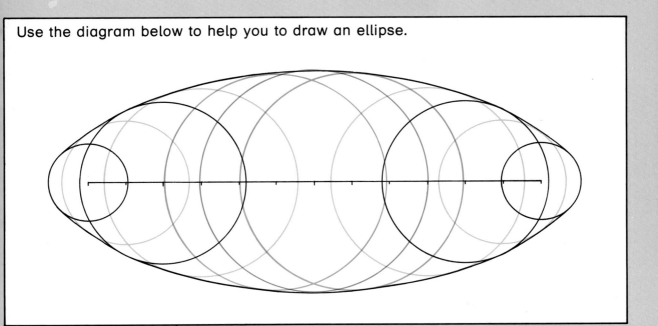

Investigations

Geostrips, fasteners, transparent cm grid, protractor

Make a square with geostrips.

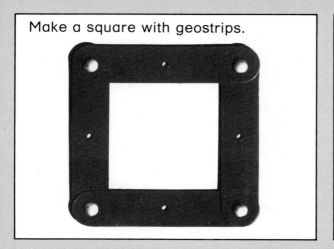

Twist the square.

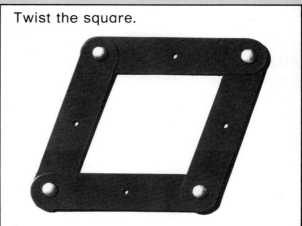

1. How many types of quadrilateral can you make?
2. Does the perimeter change?
3. Does the area change?
4. Do parallel sides remain parallel?
5. What happens to the angles?

Make lists to show which properties change on twisting and which properties remain the same.

Make a quadrilateral with all its sides of different lengths.
Twist the quadrilateral.

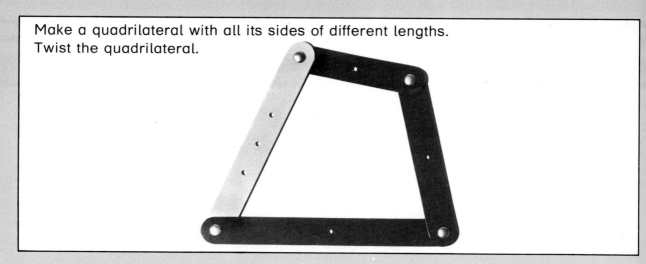

6. Can you make any right angles?
7. Can you make any parallel sides?
8. How many different types of quadrilateral can you make?

Geostrips, fasteners, cocktail sticks, balsa cement

Make each of these shapes.

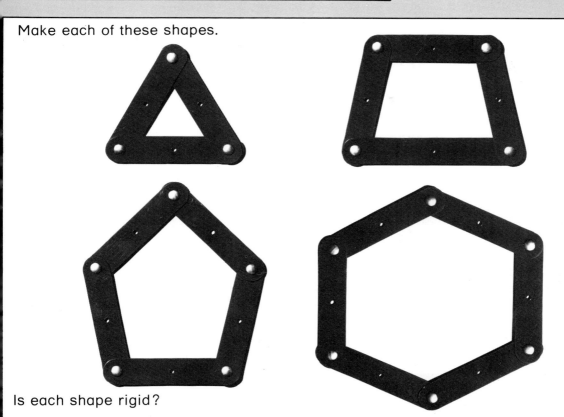

Is each shape rigid?

If a shape is not rigid, make it rigid by using further strips.
Use the least number of extra strips possible.
Draw each shape once it is rigid, including any extra strips.

What do you notice?

Make a tetrahedron with cocktail sticks and
balsa cement.   Is it rigid?
Make other "solid" shapes which are rigid.

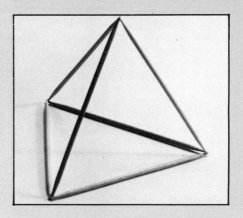

Compasses, card

Towers of Hanoi

Make three card discs of radii 25 mm, 20 mm and 15 mm.
Stack them in order of size on the red square below.
Put the smallest disc on the top.

Aim To move the three discs to the blue square.

Rules
1. A larger disc must not be placed on a smaller disc.
2. Only one disc to be moved at a time.
3. Only the top disc of a pile may be moved.
4. Discs may be placed in any of the three squares.
5. Discs cannot be placed side by side in the same square.

How many moves did it take to move the discs to the blue square?
Think of a way to record your moves.
Can you do it in a smaller number of moves?

Play the game again moving the discs to the yellow square.

Make a 10 mm disc.
Stack the four discs on the red square.
Using the same rules move them to the blue square.

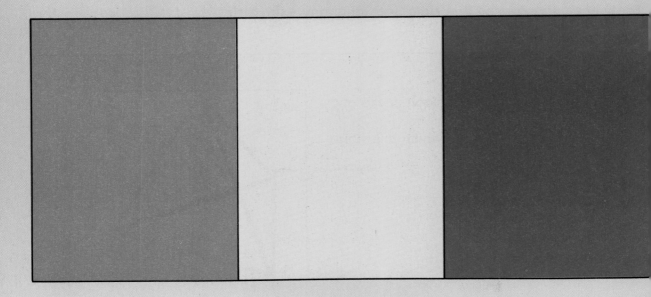

Beads, laces

Here are different ways of threading two yellow beads and one green bead.

Are there any more ways?

How many ways can you find of threading each of the following?

There are five netball teams.
Each team plays each other team twice.
Once at home and once away.
Only one game is played each week.
How many weeks will it take to play all the games?

Assessment Test

1. Add 2462, 95 and 3836.

2. Find the difference between 2973 and 6003.

3. Multiply £6·38 by 12.

4. Divide 4·770 l by 9.

5. 1512 ÷ 14

6. Put brackets in this to make it true
   1000 + 436 × 2 = 1872

7. What is 15% of £60?

8. Write 24 out of 80 as a percentage.

9. Calculate the missing angle.

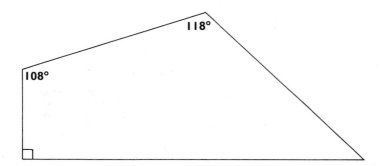

10. Divide 25·5 by 6

11. 6·25 × 1·4

12. 560 ÷ 2·8

13. Share £27 between Peter and Alan in the ratio of 5 : 4.

Find the area of these shapes.

14.

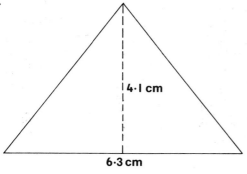

6·3 cm   4·1 cm

15.

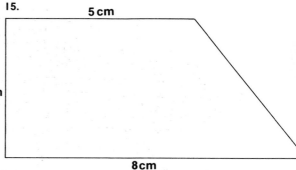

5 cm   3·8 cm   8 cm

16. $1\frac{7}{8} \times 2\frac{3}{5}$

17. $\frac{5}{6} \div \frac{3}{4}$

18. How much greater than 3^3 is 14^2?

19. Write 2·2 million in figures.

Write the names of these shapes.

20.

21.

22.

23. Calculate the circumference of a circle of radius 9 cm. (Remember $\pi = 3\cdot14$) Calculate its area.

24. What weight is $\frac{2}{3}$ of $4\frac{1}{2}$ kg?

25. If $a = 6$ and $b = 2\cdot5$ find the value of $2a + 3b$.

26. Complete this table and draw a graph to show the information.

Length of the side of a square (in cm)	1	2	3	4	5	6	7	8	9	10
Area of square (in cm²)										

Measurement

360° protractor

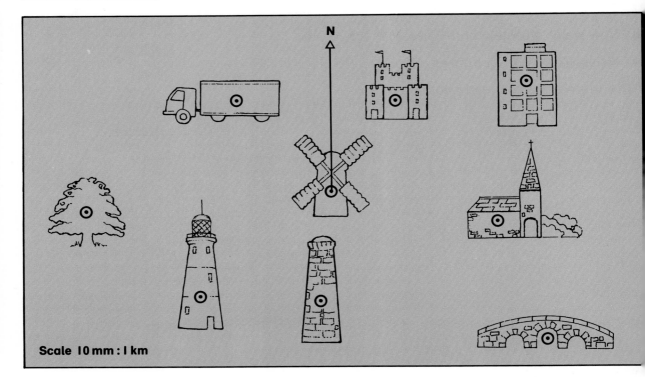

Scale 10 mm : 1 km

1. Measure the bearing of each object from the windmill.
2. How many kilometres is each object from the windmill?

The harbour is 5·8 km due north of the lighthouse.
The table shows the bearing and distance of a
ship from the lighthouse each hour.

Time	Bearing from lighthouse	Distance from lighthouse
1st hour	050°	4 km
2nd hour	085°	6 km
3rd hour	145°	5½ km
4th hour	170°	6½ km
5th hour	215°	5 km

Use the information to plot the hourly
position of the ship.

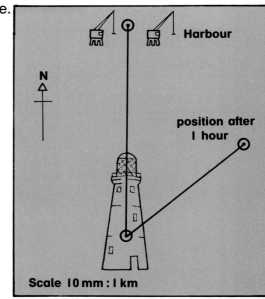

Harbour

N

position after
1 hour

Scale 10 mm : 1 km

68

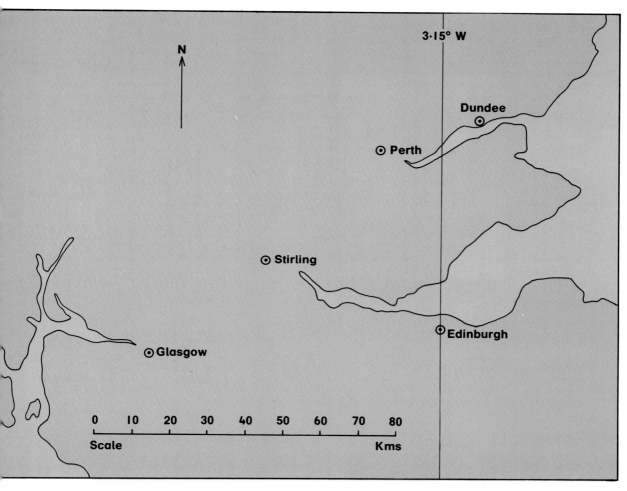

Find the bearing from Edinburgh of:
a) Glasgow.   b) Stirling.   c) Perth.   d) Dundee.

Find the distance in kilometres between:
a) Edinburgh and Glasgow.   b) Edinburgh and Dundee.
c) Stirling and Glasgow.   d) Perth and Dundee.

Number

Micematics

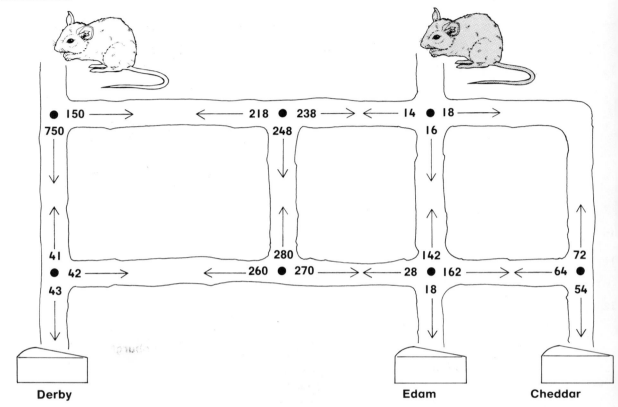

Find each mouse's route by answering these questions.

White mouse	**Black mouse**
Grams in $\frac{3}{4}$ kg	$216 \div 12$
The average of 23, 56 and 47	$\frac{2}{5}$ of 160
$\frac{2}{3}$ of 420	$(12 \times 6) + (7 \times 10)$
14×17	The average of 21, 11, 7 and 17
$208 \div 13$	Minutes between 1135 and 1543
$54 \div \frac{1}{3}$	(Prime number after 11) $\times$ 20
$72 \times \frac{3}{4}$	Difference between 1431 and 1388

Which cheese does each mouse eat?

1. Add 246, 1903, 2602 and 4137.

2. How much more than £26·50 is £31·25?

3. Find the product of 1237 and 28.

4. Find the average of £7·39, £9·47, £3·28 and £6·02.

5. Which number when divided by 36 gives an answer of 276?

6. Find the total of $3\frac{1}{4}$ l, 2·760 l and 4·75 l.

7. Find the difference between 6·5 kg and 1275 g.

8. From 6·291 take 3·59

9. Add 2·7 km, 480 m and 3·65 km.

10. How much greater than $\frac{3}{7}$ of 2464 is $\frac{5}{8}$ of 4992?

11. The adult return fare from Wingfield to London is £12·58.
    Find the cost for four adults.

12. A table costs £35·60.
    It is reduced in the sale by 15%.
    What is its sale price?

13. A TV set costs £313.
    Mr. Swift pays a deposit of £55, and pays the rest in 12 equal
    monthly payments.
    How much does he pay each month?

14. Complete this table.

Car registration number	Average speed in km	Distance travelled in km	Time taken
CVO 304 T	42	98	
KRC 291 V	48		2 hrs 10 min
HRC 601 N	35	157·5	
ANU 12 W	40		3 hrs 12 min
BMC 272 V	54	337·5	
JTC 1 W		105	2 hrs 30 min

Mr. and Mrs. Parkin are planning a holiday in Italy.
They have two daughters, 7 year old Victoria and 11 year old Charlotte.
They decide to stay near Pisa.
Here are details from their holiday brochure.

La Saline

A pleasant, modern tourist class hotel situated about 150 yards from the beach of San Ferdinando. The hotel which was first opened in 1972, is extremely well managed by an expert team of staff and offers its guests good homely Italian cuisine. Facilities include a games room, TV lounge, large bar and attractive dining room. All double rooms have their own bathrooms and there is a lift serving all four floors. Beach charges and full board are included in the cost of the holiday. Children are welcome and special menus for younger visitors can be arranged.

Villa Rimini

A very pleasant modern pensione situated near Bartolomeos beach and only a few minutes walk from the centre of Marina village. The beach is of golden sand and offers safe bathing for the whole family. The pensione is situated in two adjacent buildings and is run by the Lopez family who take a friendly and personal interest in the well-being and comfort of their guests. All the food is home-cooked and is the very best of simple Italian fare. Prices quoted include half board and there are a number of excellent restaurants on or around the beach area which offer reasonably priced midday meals. Villa Rimini has a pleasant lounge with TV and a delightful small garden with patio where guests can enjoy the warm summer evenings. All double rooms have a shower and W.C. Buses leave frequently from a stop opposite the hotel for many picturesque destinations in the surrounding countryside.

La Fortuna

La Fortuna is a large new hotel built on five storeys and offering every modern convenience and comfort to its guests. All single and double rooms have their own bathrooms and balconies and all guests have full use of the luxury swimming pool. The hotel has a first class restaurant and bar. Prices include full-board.

Costs are in pounds for each adult for 2 weeks holiday.

	23 May to 24 July		25 July to 11 Sept		12 Sept onwards	
	Rail	Air	Rail	Air	Rail	Air
Villa Rimini	220	235	230	250	215	230
Fortuna	430	480	460	520	400	450
La Saline	300	340	340	380	290	320

Reductions for children

Up to 2 yrs old – 80% reduction
Between 2 and 9 – 20% reduction
Between 9 and 12 – 15% reduction
Over 12 yrs old – no reduction

They choose the hotel "La Saline" for their two week holiday,
from 2nd August until 16th August.

1. What will be the cost for the whole family if they fly?
2. How much cheaper would it be if they went by train?

The time in Italy is one hour ahead of the time in the U.K.
When the local time in Pisa is 0900, the local time in London is 0800.

Flight timetable from Heathrow   The times given are local times.

MILAN – weekly on Saturdays

| 12.50 dep. | ↓ | HEATHROW | ↑ | arr. 18.50 |
| 15.40 arr. | | MILAN | | dep. 18.00 |

ROME – weekly on Saturdays

| 12.00 dep. | ↓ | HEATHROW | ↑ | arr. 18.15 |
| 15.20 arr. | | ROME | | dep. 16.45 |

PISA – weekly on Sundays

| 12.00 dep. | ↓ | HEATHROW | ↑ | arr. 21.55 |
| 15.00 arr. | | PISA | | dep. 20.50 |

VENICE – weekly on Saturdays

| 09.50 dep. | ↓ | HEATHROW | ↑ | arr. 11.00 |
| 12.55 arr. | | VENICE | | dep. 10.00 |

3. How long is the flight from Heathrow to Pisa?
4. How long is the flight from Pisa to Heathrow?

While Mr. and Mrs. Parkin are on holiday they hope to hire a car for 12 days.
Here are the details sent by their travel agent.

CAR HIRE

Type of car	Normal daily rate	Special daily rate minimum 7 days hire	Insurance £1.20 per day extra.
Fiat 127	£16	£13	
Fiat Ritmo	£20	£16	
Fiat 131 L	£24	£20	
Fiat 132	£32	£26	

5. What would be the cost of hiring a Fiat Ritmo for 12 days?
   Remember to include the insurance charge.
6. What would be the cost if the normal daily rate was charged?

Area

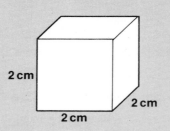

1. Find the area of a face of this cube.

2. Find the total area of its 6 faces.

The total area is called the **surface area**.

3. Find the surface area of these shapes.
   Remember each shape has 6 faces.

A

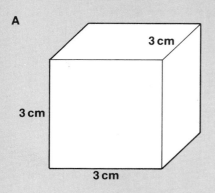

B

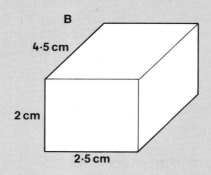

C

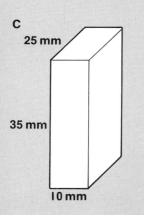

D

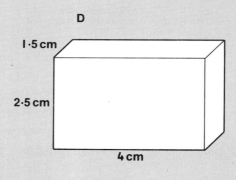

4. Calculate the surface area of Shape A if the length of each side is doubled.

5. Now do the same for Shapes B and C.

6. How many times greater is the surface area of a cuboid when the length of each side is doubled?

7. What happens to the surface area of a cuboid if the length of each side is halved?

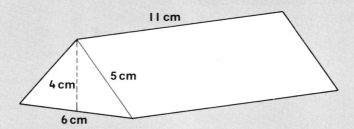

1. Find the area of the triangular face of this prism.

2. Find the total area of its 2 triangular faces.

3. Find the area of each rectangular face.

4. Find the total area of its 3 rectangular faces.

5. What is its total surface area?

6. How many times greater is its surface area if its measurements are doubled?

7. How many times smaller is its surface area if its measurements are halved?

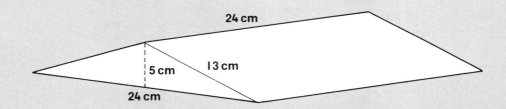

8. Calculate the surface area of this prism.

9. If its measurements are doubled, what do you think its surface area will be? Check your answer by working it out.

10. If its measurements are halved, what do you think its new surface area will be? Check your answer by working it out.

What is the length of one side of a cube with a surface area of:

11. 96 cm²?   12. 54 cm²?

Percentages

Mr. Jackson owns a grocer's shop. He buys his stock from a warehouse. He bought some beans. The more he bought the cheaper they were.

The beans cost 20p a tin.
The warehouse gave the following discount:

51–100 tins 5%
101–200 tins 8%
201–500 tins 10%
More than 500 tins 15%

1. What is the cost of:
   a) 80 tins? b) 150 tins?
   c) 400 tins? d) 600 tins?

Mr. Jackson sells each tin of beans for 25p.
2. How much profit does he make on:
   a) 80 tins? b) 150 tins?
   c) 400 tins? d) 600 tins?

Mr. Jackson also bought some boxes of crisps.
Each box holds 48 packets of crisps.

No. of boxes bought	Flavour
12	Salt and vinegar
9	Chicken
5	Prawn
14	Beef
8	Cheese and onion

3. How many packets of crisps did he buy of each flavour?

4. What was the total number of packets bought?

5. Each packet of crisps was sold for 12p. What was the total amount he received for the crisps?

6. He paid £4·50 for each box of crisps.
   How much profit did he make altogether?

76

This is Mr. and Mrs. Bellemy's deposit account book.

10% interest.

Date	Details	Withdrawals	Deposits	Balance
	Mr & Mrs Bellemy		a/c No. 47386	
1.1.78	Cash		200.00	200.00
31-12-78	Interest		20.00	220.00
31-12.79	Interest.			
31.12.80	Interest			

1. How much interest did Mr. and Mrs. Bellemy receive on 31st Dec. 1979?
2. How much was in their account on 1st Jan. 1980?
3. How much interest did Mr. and Mrs. Bellemy receive on 31st Dec. 1980?
4. How much was in their account on 1st Jan. 1981?
5. What was the total amount of interest received over the three years?

6. This is Mr. and Mrs. Chadwick's bank book.
   Complete the missing entries.

Date	Details	Withdrawals	Deposits	Balance
	Mr & Mrs Chadwick		a/c No. 627483	
7-2-80	Cash		500.00	500.00
3.3.80	Cheque	113.20		?
4.5.80	Cash		27.50	414.30
17.5.80	Cash	?		233.30
28.10.80	Cash		147.65	?
31.12.80	Interest		19.05	?

Decimals

Complete these:

1. $2 \cdot 3 \times \square = 23$

2. $0 \cdot 49 \times \square = 49$

3. $0 \cdot 07 \times \square = 70$

4. $14 \cdot 5 \times \square = 145$

5. $0 \cdot 143 \times \square = 143$

6. $0 \cdot 274 \times \square = 2 \cdot 74$

7. $6 \cdot 59 \div \square = 0 \cdot 659$

8. $320 \div \square = 0 \cdot 32$

9. $59 \cdot 1 \div \square = 0 \cdot 591$

10. $1212 \div \square = 121 \cdot 2$

11. $17 \cdot 8 \div \square = 0 \cdot 178$

12. $400 \div \square = 0 \cdot 4$

13. $\square \times 10 = 14 \cdot 7$

14. $\square \times 100 = 4$

15. $\square \div 100 = 0 \cdot 89$

16. $\square \div 1000 = 0 \cdot 076$

Fractions can be changed into decimals by dividing
the numerator by the denominator.

Change $\frac{3}{4}$ into a decimal.

$$\begin{array}{r} 0 \cdot 7\,5 \\ 4\,\overline{)\,3 \cdot 0\,0} \end{array} \quad \frac{3}{4} = 0 \cdot 75$$

$1\frac{3}{4} = 1 \cdot 75$

Change $\frac{1}{8}$ into a decimal.

$$\begin{array}{r} 0 \cdot 1\,2\,5 \\ 8\,\overline{)\,1 \cdot 0\,0\,0} \end{array} \quad \frac{1}{8} = 0 \cdot 125$$

$1\frac{1}{8} = 1 \cdot 125$

Write these as decimals.

17. $\frac{5}{8}$

18. $\frac{2}{5}$

19. $\frac{7}{8}$

20. $\frac{3}{5}$

21. $5\frac{7}{10}$

22. $\frac{3}{20}$

23. $1\frac{2}{5}$

24. $3\frac{9}{10}$

25. $4\frac{5}{8}$

26. $5\frac{7}{8}$

27. $1\frac{7}{20}$

28. $2\frac{3}{5}$

Some fractions cannot be changed accurately into decimals.
The decimal numbers form a repeating pattern.

Change $\frac{2}{11}$ into a decimal.

$$\begin{array}{r} 0 \cdot 1\,8\,1\,8\,1\,8 \\ 11\,\overline{)\,2 \cdot 0\,0\,0\,0\,0\,0} \end{array} \quad \frac{2}{11} = 0 \cdot 181818$$

Find the pattern when you change these fractions into decimals.

29. $\frac{1}{3}$

30. $\frac{1}{11}$

31. $\frac{4}{9}$

32. $\frac{7}{11}$

33. $\frac{1}{6}$

34. $\frac{8}{9}$

35. $\frac{3}{11}$

36. $\frac{5}{11}$

37. $\frac{5}{6}$

38. $\frac{2}{3}$

39. $\frac{1}{7}$

40. $\frac{3}{7}$

1. $\begin{array}{r} 15 \cdot 7 \\ 1 \cdot 38 \\ + 12 \cdot 8 \\ \hline \end{array}$
2. $\begin{array}{r} 17 \cdot 45 \\ - 2 \cdot 68 \\ \hline \end{array}$
3. $\begin{array}{r} 0 \cdot 234 \\ \times 8 \\ \hline \end{array}$
4. $9 \overline{)110 \cdot 7}$

5. $1 \cdot 47 \times 2 \cdot 3$
6. $27 \cdot 04 \times 4 \cdot 9$
7. $172 \cdot 6 - 93 \cdot 27$
8. $33 \cdot 5 + 27 \cdot 39$
9. $120 \times 7 \cdot 9$
10. $2 \cdot 94 \times 5 \cdot 6$

11. Add together 0·478, 16·09 and 124·2.

12. What must be added to 0·074 to make 0·412?

13. Find the product of 3·9 and 1·74.

14. Divide 243 by 2·7.

Ask your teacher how to approximate to 1 decimal place, 2 decimal places, and 3 decimal places.

Work these out to 1 decimal place.

15. $7 \overline{)148 \cdot 21}$
16. $9 \overline{)27 \cdot 93}$
17. $8 \overline{)19 \cdot 78}$
18. $5 \overline{)37 \cdot 3}$
19. $7 \overline{)52 \cdot 94}$
20. $3 \overline{)1 \cdot 74}$

Work these out to 2 decimal places.

21. $6 \overline{)5 \cdot 782}$
22. $4 \overline{)0 \cdot 493}$
23. $9 \overline{)15 \cdot 07}$
24. $8 \overline{)9 \cdot 7}$
25. $5 \overline{)23 \cdot 74}$
26. $6 \overline{)19 \cdot 06}$

Work these out to 3 decimal places.

27. $7 \overline{)5 \cdot 078}$
28. $3 \overline{)0 \cdot 409}$
29. $9 \overline{)52 \cdot 9}$
30. $7 \overline{)148}$
31. $4 \overline{)0 \cdot 29}$
32. $8 \overline{)17 \cdot 05}$

Change these fractions into decimals.
Write each answer to 3 decimal places.

33. $3\frac{1}{3}$
34. $2\frac{1}{11}$
35. $3\frac{5}{8}$
36. $1\frac{4}{9}$
37. $4\frac{1}{6}$
38. $2\frac{8}{9}$

39. $1\frac{5}{6}$
40. $2\frac{3}{7}$
41. $2\frac{3}{8}$
42. $3\frac{2}{3}$
43. $5\frac{3}{11}$
44. $1\frac{1}{7}$

Graphs

A goods train left Scampton at 1300 hours.
It travelled for one hour.
It had to stop three times for signals, at 1310, 1325 and 1350.
At each signal it stopped for exactly five minutes.
Between the stops it travelled at an average speed of 60 km an hour.

Complete the graph to show its progress.

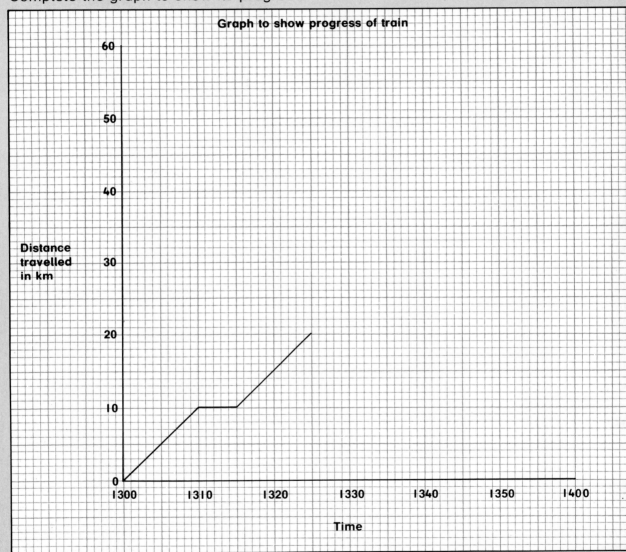

A passenger train left Scampton at 1320.
It travelled for 40 minutes without stopping.
Its average speed was 90 km an hour.
On the same axes, draw a graph to show the progress of the passenger train.

Answer these questions from the graph.

1. How far did the goods train travel in the hour?

2. How far had it travelled by 1320?

3. How far from Scampton was the goods train at 1335?

4. How far had the passenger train travelled by 1400?

5. How far from Scampton was it at 1325?

6. Which train was nearer to Scampton at 1330?

7. Which train was further away from Scampton at 1350?

8. At what times were the trains 5 km apart?

9. At what times were the trains 15 km apart?

10. At what time was the goods train 35 km from Scampton?

11. At what time was the passenger train 45 km from Scampton?

12. How far was the passenger train from Scampton when it overtook the goods train?

Algebra

Complete these tables.

1.  △ = ☐ + 3

△						
☐	0	1	2	3	4	5

2. △ = ☐ + 1

△						
☐	0	1	2	3	4	5

3. 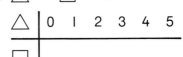 △ = ☐ − 2

△	0	1	2	3	4	5
☐						

Show all this information on one set of axes.
What do you notice?

Complete the table for each of these graphs.

4.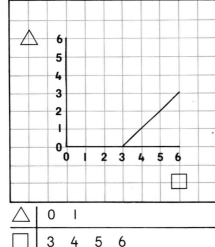

△	0	1			
☐	3	4	5	6	

5.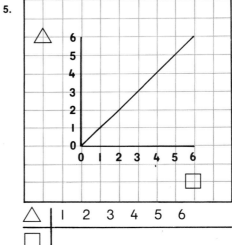

△	1	2	3	4	5	6
☐						

6.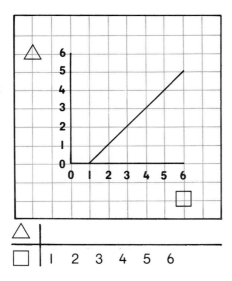

△						
☐	1	2	3	4	5	6

7.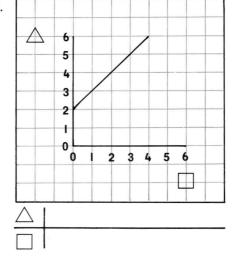

△						
☐						

82

Draw graphs to show:

1. $\triangle + \square = 4$

$\triangle$	0	1	2	3	4
$\square$					

2. $\triangle - \square = 2$

$\triangle$	2	3	4	5	6
$\square$					

3. $\triangle - \square = 0$

$\triangle$						
$\square$	0	1	2	3	4	5

4. $4 \triangle = \square$

What is the value of $\triangle$ if:

$\square = 0, 4, 8, 12, 16$?

5. $5 \triangle = \square$

What is the value of $\square$ if:

$\triangle = 0, 1, 2, 3, 4$?

6. $\triangle = 4 \square$

What is the value of $\triangle$ if:

$\square = 0, 1, 2, 3, 4$?

7. $\triangle = 5 \square$

What is the value of $\triangle$ if:

$\square = 0, 1, 2, 3, 4$?

Complete these tables.

8. $\triangle = 2 \square$

$\triangle$					
$\square$	0	1	2	3	4

9. $\triangle = 3 \square$

$\triangle$					
$\square$	0	1	2	3	4

10. $2 \triangle = \square$

$\triangle$	0	1	2	3	4
$\square$					

11. $3 \triangle = \square$

$\triangle$	0	1	2	3	4
$\square$					

Show the four sets of information on one set of axes.

What do you notice?

Number

Every cricketer likes to score a century, or 100 runs.
Some runs are scored by running between wickets.
Other runs are scored by hitting boundaries.
A boundary hit is worth either 4 or 6.

Mr. Lewis scored 100 runs.
He scored 54 by running.
The rest were scored by hitting 11 boundaries.

1. How many of his boundaries were worth 4?
2. How many of his boundaries were worth 6?

Mrs. Flint plays ladies' cricket.
She scored 102 runs.
She scored 80 by running.
She scored more boundaries worth 6 than worth 4.

3. How many boundaries did she score?

Can you make a hundred?

Rules   A. You must use all the digits 0 to 9 once.
  B. You can use any of the signs, $+ - \times \div$ as often as you want.

Here are 2 ways to make a hundred.

$98 + 7 - 6 + 5 - 4 + 3 - 2 - 1 + 0 = 100$

$(9 \times 8) + (3 \times 7) + 6 + \frac{2}{4} + \frac{5}{10} = 100$

Find as many ways as you can to make a hundred.

The cricket cup for village teams was won last year by Entwall.
This table shows details of the team's most successful batsmen in the competition.

Name	Total no. of runs scored	No. of innings completed
K. Selby	372	9
F. Martin	354	8
I. Buck	307	8
F. Elliott	299	7
S. Smith	285	6

To find a batsman's average, divide the number of runs he has scored by the number of innings he has completed.

1. Work out each batsman's average (to 2 decimal places).
2. Who was the most successful batsman?

This table shows details of the team's most successful bowlers in the competition.

Name	No. of runs scored off his bowling	No. of wickets taken
D. Peck	583	28
B. Swift	497	22
T. Mythen	462	19
G. Parkin	475	23
D. Smith	429	15

To find a bowler's average, divide the number of runs scored off him, by the number of wickets he has taken.

3. Work out each bowler's average (to 2 decimal places).
4. Who was the most successful bowler?

Shape

These shapes have been photographed from an unusual angle.
Write which shape you think each is.

1.

2.

3.

4.

Write whether each statement is true or false.

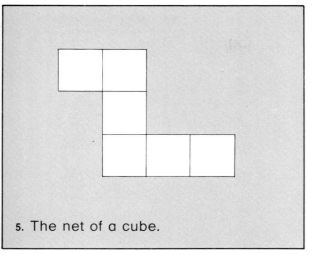

5. The net of a cube.

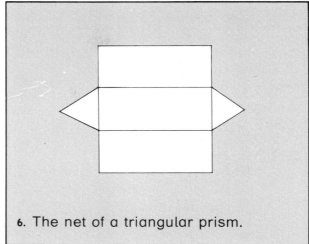

6. The net of a triangular prism.

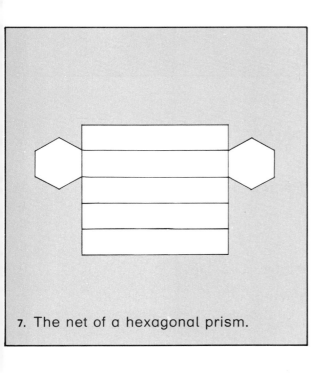

7. The net of a hexagonal prism.

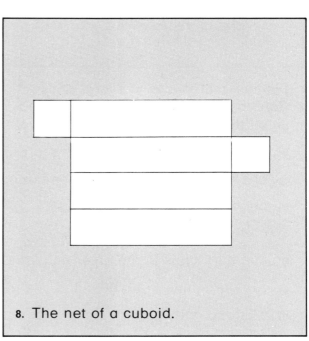

8. The net of a cuboid.

Number

A dart-board is divided into segments.
Each segment has a number.
The outer circle counts double the number.
The inner circle counts treble the number.
The outer bull counts 25.
The inner bull counts 50.
All the other parts count single.
Every player throws three darts.

The darts in the board score
treble 20 (60), double 12 (24) and 16.
The three darts have scored 100.

1. Find six more ways to score 100.
2. Can you score 100 if:
   a) all three darts land in some part of the bull?

   b) all three darts land in single scores?

   c) one dart lands in a double, one in a treble, and one in a single?

   d) all three darts land in trebles?

   e) all three darts land in doubles?

   f) one dart lands in the outer bull, and two land in doubles?

   g) two darts land in trebles, and one in the inner bull?

   h) all three darts land in one number segment?

   i) all three darts land in an odd number segment?

   j) all three darts land in the same double?

3. What is the largest score possible?

4. Which numbers cannot be scored with three darts?

   (A clue – most numbers are over 160.)

This table shows the approximate weights of coins.

1p	2p	5p	10p
3·6 g	7·2 g	5·7 g	11·4 g

1. Find the weight of 20p worth of 1p coins.
2. Find the weight of 20p worth of 2p coins. What do you notice?

3. Find the weight of £1 worth of 5p coins.
4. Find the weight of £1 worth of 10p coins. What do you notice?

5. What is the weight of £1 worth of bronze coins?
6. What is the weight of £10 worth of silver coins?

7. Complete this table.

Type of coins	Weight of coins	Value of coins
1p		£5
2p		£7·50
5p	399 g	
10p		£23

8. I have 180 g of bronze coins. How much money have I?
9. I have 684 g of silver coins. How much money have I?

A group of mixed coins weigh 237 g. The silver coins weigh 57 g.
10. What is the weight of the bronze coins?
11. What is the value of the bronze coins?
12. How much money have I altogether?

Measurement

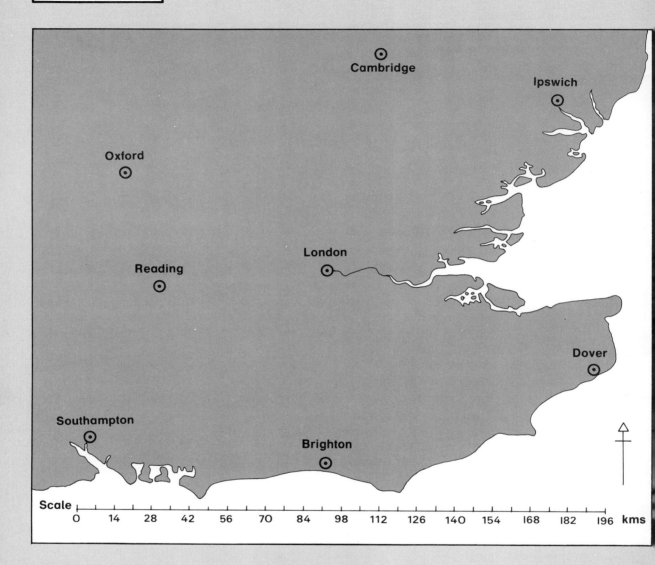

Which town is:

1. Approximately 105 km from London, bearing 110°?

2. Approximately 91 km from Brighton, bearing 317°?

3. Approximately 105 km from Oxford, bearing 064°?

4. Approximately 189 km from Southampton, bearing 081°?

5. Approximately 165 km from Ipswich, bearing 211°?

6. Approximately 165 km from Reading, bearing 101°?

James used his compass to plot his route around the park.
Measure the distances and bearings of each stage of his journey.

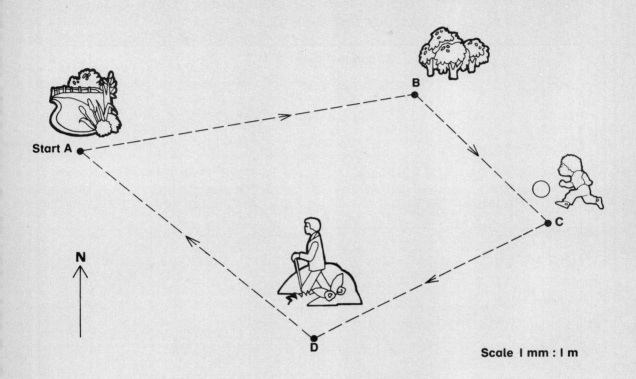

Scale 1 mm : 1 m

The next day he went for a walk.
This is the route he took.

Home to lake	Bearing 150° distance 500 m.
Lake to windmill	Bearing 88° distance 900 m.
Windmill to wood	Bearing 350° distance 600 m.
Wood to home	Bearing 259° distance 110 m.

Using a scale of 1 mm : 10 m, plot his route.

Graphs

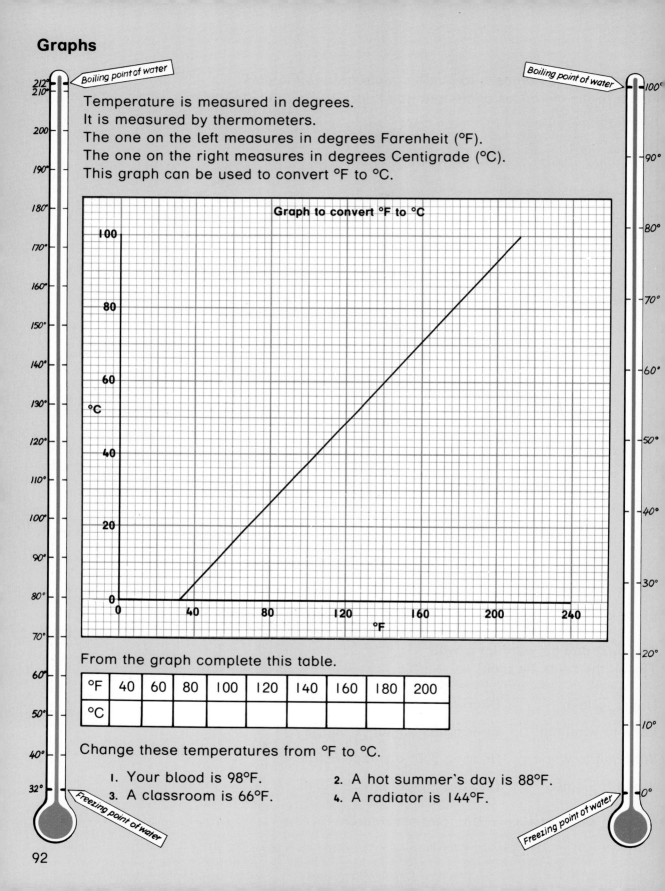

Temperature is measured in degrees.
It is measured by thermometers.
The one on the left measures in degrees Farenheit (°F).
The one on the right measures in degrees Centigrade (°C).
This graph can be used to convert °F to °C.

Graph to convert °F to °C

From the graph complete this table.

°F	40	60	80	100	120	140	160	180	200
°C									

Change these temperatures from °F to °C.

1. Your blood is 98°F.
2. A hot summer's day is 88°F.
3. A classroom is 66°F.
4. A radiator is 144°F.

92

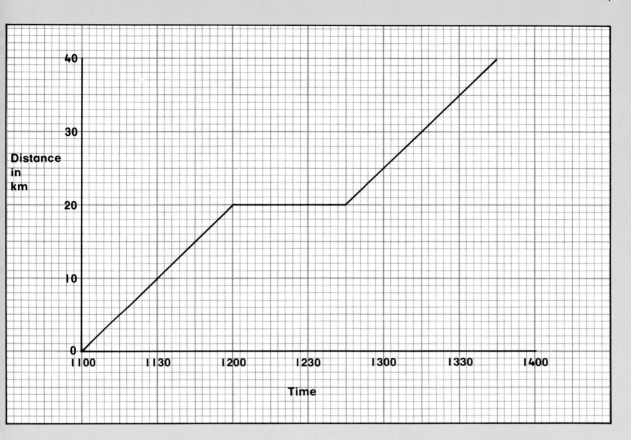

These graphs are not complete.

They have labels missing.

Decide what each graph represents.

Copy the graphs and complete the labels.

Prepare a table of information from which they could have been drawn.

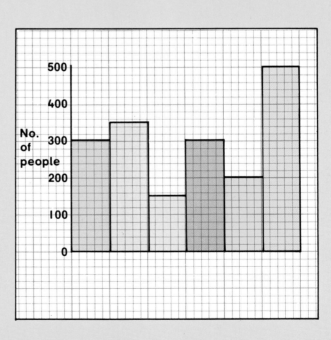

Decimals

1. Find the average height of five children measuring 1·45 m, 1·39 m, 1·06 m, 0·98 m and 1·27 m.
2. Find the width of a rectangle having a length of 5·4 cm and an area of 27 cm².
3. A cuboid's measurements are: width 3·8 cm, length 5·2 cm, and height 7·9 cm. What is its volume?
4. Put these in order beginning with the largest.

$$2\frac{4}{9}, \ 2·54, \ 2\frac{5}{11}, \ 2\frac{3}{7}$$

53·1 ÷ 0·9

Make the divisor a whole number.

Multiply each number by 10.

(53·1 × 10) ÷ (0·9 × 10)

$$
\begin{array}{r}
59 \\
9\overline{)531}
\end{array}
$$

531 ÷ 9

53·1 ÷ 0·9 = 59

---

5. 39·2 ÷ 0·8	6. 78·3 ÷ 0·9	7. 39·2 ÷ 0·7
8. 68·9 ÷ 1·3	9. 81·9 ÷ 2·1	10. 271·6 ÷ 2·8
11. 15·68 ÷ 3·2	12. 5·13 ÷ 1·9	13. 26·46 ÷ 4·2
14. 14·11 ÷ 1·7	15. 10·5 ÷ 1·5	16. 14·82 ÷ 3·8

16·9 ÷ 0·13

Make the divisor a whole number.

Multiply each number by 100.

(16·9 × 100) ÷ (0·13 × 100)

$$
\begin{array}{r}
130 \\
13\overline{)1690}
\end{array}
$$

1690 ÷ 13

16·9 ÷ 0·13 = 130

---

17. 2·31 ÷ 0·21	18. 22·5 ÷ 0·15	19. 16 ÷ 0·32
20. 30·48 ÷ 0·12	21. 82·8 ÷ 0·36	22. 17·68 ÷ 0·17
23. 4·5 ÷ 0·09	24. 6·732 ÷ 0·17	25. 32·19 ÷ 0·87
26. 58·52 ÷ 0·19	27. 5·336 ÷ 0·23	28. 1·92 ÷ 0·24

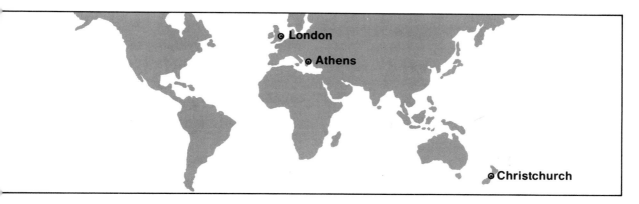

Here are the average monthly temperatures for London.

	Jan.	Feb.	Mar.	Apr.	May	Jun.	Jul.	Aug.	Sept.	Oct.	Nov.	Dec.
Temp. in °C	3·9	5·6	8·3	11·7	13·3	15·0	16·7	16·1	13·9	11·1	8·3	5·6

1. Draw a graph to show these temperatures.

These are the temperature graphs of the other two cities marked on the map.

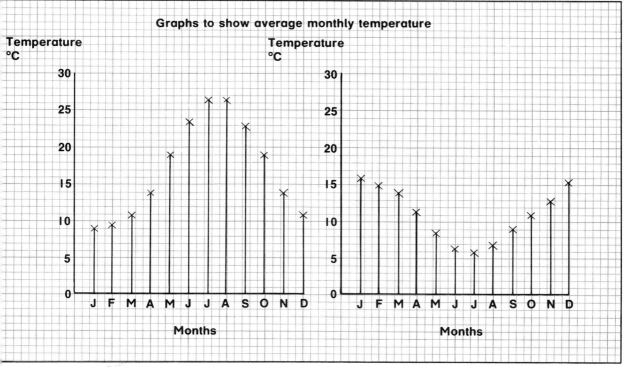

2. Which graph do you think shows the monthly temperatures of Christchurch?

Percentages

Mr. Badger, Mr. Jacob and Mr. Fowler bought a car each.
Mr. Badger's car cost £1250.
Mr. Jacob's car cost £1000.
Mr. Fowler's car cost £1500.

They could not afford to pay for the cars so they borrowed money from the Jenkin's Finance Company.

Mr. Badger had a one year loan.
He repaid £114·58 each month.

Mr. Jacob had a two year loan.
He repaid £48·12 each month.

Mr. Fowler had a three year loan.
He repaid £50·55 each month.

1. How much had each man paid to the finance company at the end of his loan?

2. How much more had Mr. Fowler paid than Mr. Badger?

Each car loses 20% of its value each year.

3. How much was each car worth after one year?

4. How much was each car worth after two years?

5. How much was each car worth after three years?

Measurement

Peter and Janet wanted to find the height of their school.
Janet stood where she could see the highest part of the school and measured its angle of elevation. It was 35°.
From where Janet was standing Peter measured a distance of 10 metres. From this new position Janet again measured the angle of elevation. It was 25°.
Peter measured the height of Janet's eyes from the ground. It was 1·5 m.

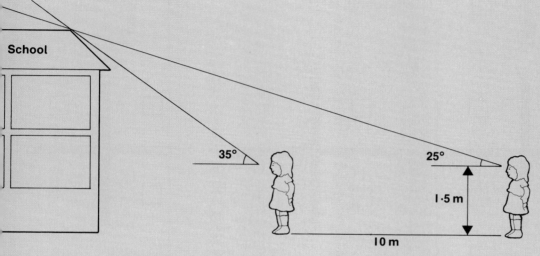

In the classroom they made a scale drawing to find the height of the school. They chose a scale of 5 mm : 1 m.

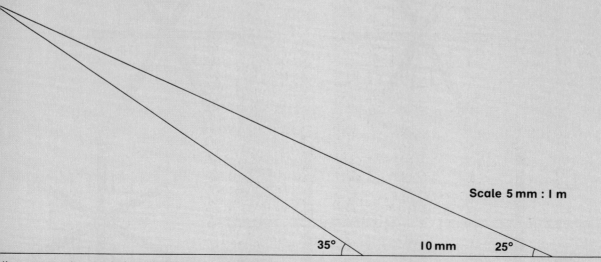

Scale 5 mm : 1 m

What was the height of Janet and Peter's school?
Do not forget to add on the height of Janet's eyes.
Now you find the height of a tall building in the same way.

97

Number

Addition, subtraction, multiplication and division are number operations.

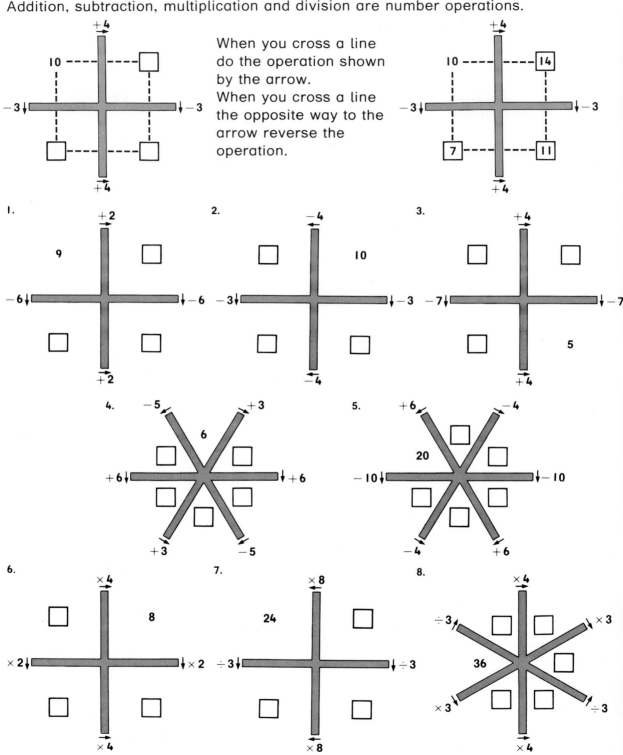

When you cross a line do the operation shown by the arrow.
When you cross a line the opposite way to the arrow reverse the operation.

Complete these:
Remember the direction of the arrow is important.

1.

2.

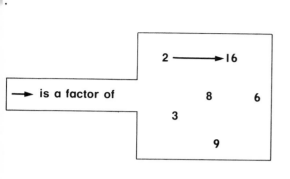

Write the relationship shown by these arrows.

3.   4.

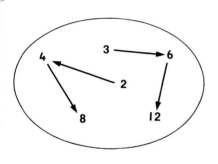   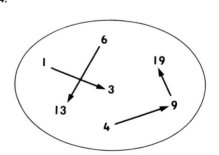

5.   6.

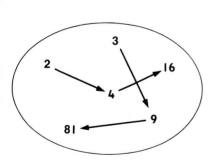   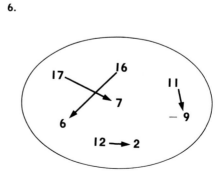

Write the new relationship for each diagram if the arrow is reversed.

Measurement

360° protractor

This is Black Bert's treasure map. Somewhere on Shuteye Island he buried his treasure, but died before he could dig it up. Can you find where he buried it using the information on the map?

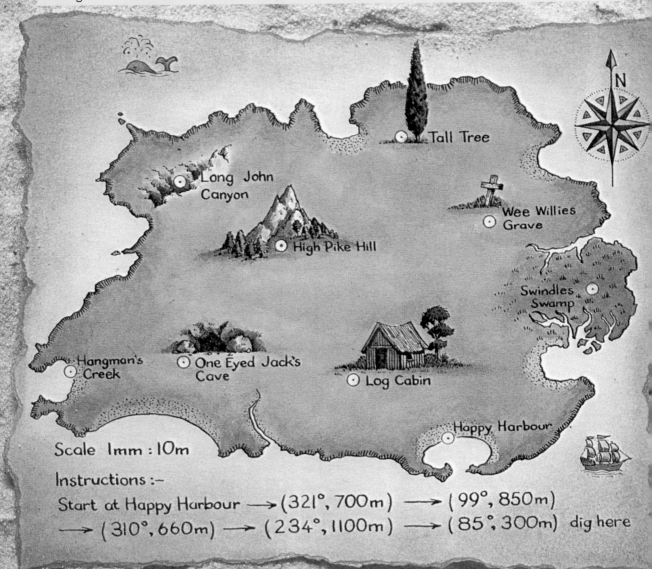

Scale 1mm : 10m

Instructions :-

Start at Happy Harbour ⟶ (321°, 700m) ⟶ (99°, 850m)
⟶ (310°, 660m) ⟶ (234°, 1100m) ⟶ (85°, 300m) dig here

Make a treasure map of your own, and ask your friend if she/he can find your hidden treasure.

Cotton, weights, plastic carton

Petra and Sharon found the breaking strain of a
300 mm length of cotton.

They used a yogurt pot as a container for the weights.
The pot was so light that they decided to ignore
its weight.

Cotton was fastened onto the pot.
It was hung on a stand so that exactly 300 mm of
cotton was hanging down.

300 mm

Weights were added in 50 g stages until the cotton broke.
They repeated the experiment four more times with
pieces of cotton of the same length to see if they always
broke at the same weight.

Here is a graph showing their results.

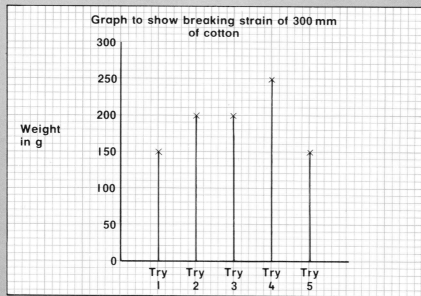

Graph to show breaking strain of 300 mm of cotton

Weight in g (vertical axis: 0, 50, 100, 150, 200, 250, 300)

Try 1: 150
Try 2: 200
Try 3: 200
Try 4: 250
Try 5: 150

1. Calculate the average breaking strain of their 300 mm
   lengths of cotton.
2. Do the experiment yourself to find the average breaking
   strain of a 300 mm length of cotton.
3. Will a 150 mm length of cotton break at the same
   weight as 300 mm?

Graphs

Ian and his father were throwing a ball to each other.
This graph shows what happened to the ball when Ian's father threw it.

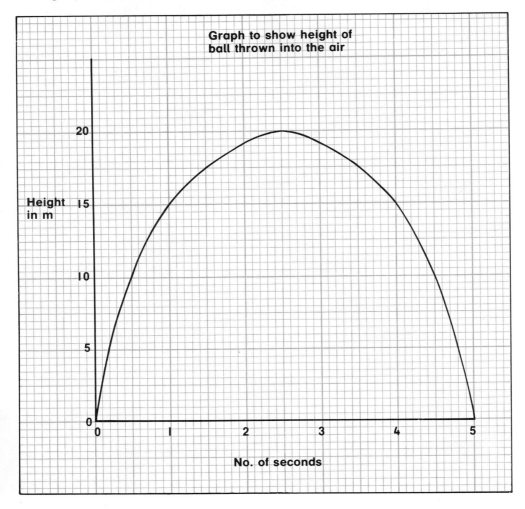

Graph to show height of ball thrown into the air

Height in m

No. of seconds

1. How long was the ball in the air?
2. How long was it travelling upwards?
3. How long was it travelling downwards?
4. What was the greatest height it reached?
5. How high was it after
   1 second?   2 seconds?   3 seconds?   4 seconds?

6. How high was it after
   1·2 seconds?   1·5 seconds?   4·5 seconds?

7. How long had it been in the air when it was
   10 m high?   5 m high?   20 m high?

Mr. Jones wanted to make a rectangular flower garden.
He had 20 m of fencing, including a gate.
He wanted to arrange the fencing to give him the largest possible area of garden.
He started to work it out like this:

Length of garden in m	1	2	3	4	5	6	7	8	9
Width of garden in m	9	8	7	6	5	4	3	2	1
Perimeter of garden in m	20	20	20						
Area of garden in m²	9	16	21						

Complete the table for him.
Complete this graph to show information from the table.

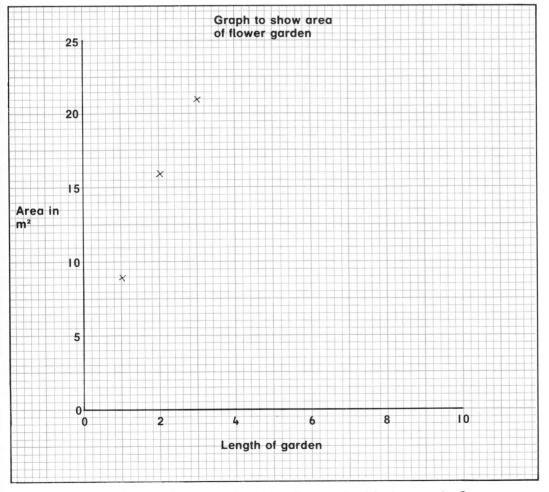

Graph to show area of flower garden

What was the shape of the garden Mr. Jones decided to make?

Percentages

Mr. and Mrs. Taylor wanted to buy a new dining suite, but they did not have enough money to pay cash.

Elms
FURNITURE STORE

Dining Suite   £1200

$\frac{1}{3}$ Deposit

5% Interest charge on
remaining money

JASPER'S STORE

Dining suite £1200

$\frac{1}{4}$ deposit

8% Interest charge on

remaining money

Some stores ask customers to pay part of the cost as a deposit. The remaining balance is paid with interest within a year.

This is how much Mr. and Mrs. Taylor would pay at the Elms Furniture Store.

1. What is the total cost of the dining suite bought from Jasper's store?

2. Which store offers the better bargain?

Elms
FURNITURE STORE

	ACCOUNT
Cost of dining suite £ 1200	£
Deposit $\frac{1}{3}$ of £ 1200	400
Balance remaining	800
Interest (5% on £800)	40
Total cost of suite	1240

Find the total cost of these items.

1. 3 piece suite

Cash price £1600
$\frac{1}{4}$ deposit
6% interest charge

2. Television set

Cash price £600
20% deposit
8% interest charge

3. New car

Cash price £5400
$\frac{1}{5}$ deposit
12% interest charge

4. Caravan

Cash price £3280
$\frac{1}{4}$ deposit
5% interest charge

5. Video cassette recorder

Cash price £700
15% deposit
10% interest charge

6. Motorcycle

Cash price £1500
$\frac{1}{3}$ deposit
17% interest charge

7. Camera

Cash price £210
$\frac{1}{3}$ deposit
10% interest charge

8. Dinghy

Cash price £900
20% deposit
5% interest charge

9. Diamond necklace

Cash price £2400
40% deposit
15% interest charge

Estate agents sell houses for people.
The amount they charge depends on
the price of the house.

Estate Agents' charges
3% on the first £10 000
2% on the next   £5 000
1% on any amount remaining

The price of this house
is £16 000.

This is the Estate Agents' bill.

Value of house	£16 000	
		£
3% of	£10 000	300
2% of	£5 000	100
1% of	£1 000	10
	Charge	410

How much will the estate agent charge on these houses?

1. £18 500

2. £8 250

3. £36 900

4. £27 200

5. £59 750

6. £75 800

Measurement

Find the capacity of the can in ml.
Write the volume of the can in cm³.

Measure the diameter of the can in cm.
Find its radius.
Calculate the area of its base (π = 3·14).
Measure the height of the can in cm.

Volume = area of base × height.

Calculate the volume of the can.
Compare this answer with the volume
you found by measuring.

1. Which do you think is the more
   accurate answer?

Calculate the volume of each of these.

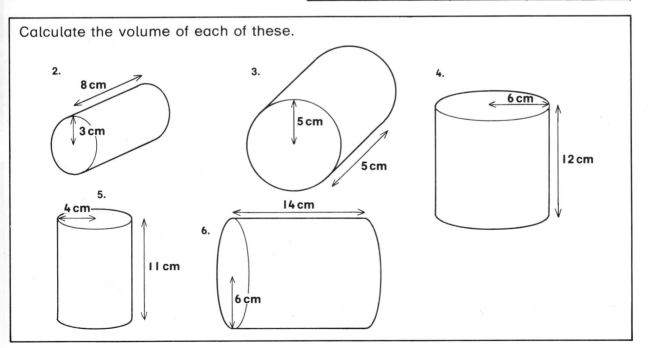

2.   8 cm   3 cm

3.   5 cm   5 cm

4.   6 cm   12 cm

5.   4 cm   11 cm

6.   14 cm   6 cm

107

Number

Remember $5 \times 5 \times 5$ can be written as 5^3

Now write these in the shorthand way.

1. $10 \times 10 \times 10 \times 10$ 2. $8 \times 8 \times 8$
3. $6 \times 6 \times 6 \times 6 \times 6 \times 6$
4. $2 \times 2 \times 2 \times 2$ 5. $4 \times 4 \times 4 \times 4$
6. $10 \times 10 \times 10 \times 10 \times 10 \times 10$

We can use this shorthand to write very large numbers.

$100\,000 = 10^5$ $1\,000\,000 = 10^6$
$400\,000 = 4 \times 10^5$ $8\,000\,000 = 8 \times 10^6$

7. Here are the approximate distances
   of the planets from the sun.
   Write them in the shorthand way.

	Distance in km
Mercury	9 000 000
Venus	100 000 000
Earth	150 000 000
Mars	230 000 000
Jupiter	770 000 000
Saturn	1 400 000 000
Uranus	2 900 000 000
Neptune	4 500 000 000
Pluto	5 900 000 000

8. Here are some facts about the moon.
   Write the numbers in full.

Diameter $\simeq 4 \times 10^3$ km

Surface area $\simeq 4 \times 10^7$ km^2

Weight $\simeq 8 \times 10^{19}$ tonnes

Number of visible craters $\simeq 3 \times 10^4$

Square roots

Write the value of:

1. $\sqrt{25}$ 2. $\sqrt{49}$ 3. $\sqrt{81}$ 4. $\sqrt{121}$ 5. $\sqrt{144}$

Choose the most sensible answer.

6. $\sqrt{43}$ = (9·42, 6·56, 4·23)   7. $\sqrt{50}$ = (7·07, 6·82, 8·41)

8. $\sqrt{14}$ = (2·65, 4·44, 3·74)

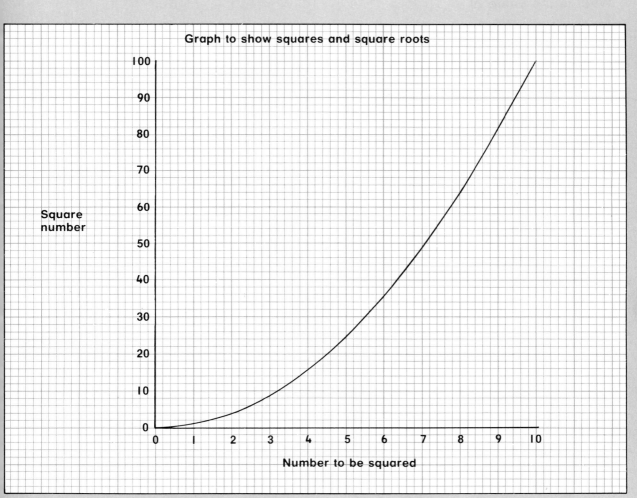

Graph to show squares and square roots

From the graph find the approximate values of these:

9. $\sqrt{10}$ 10. $\sqrt{26}$ 11. $\sqrt{48}$ 12. $\sqrt{61}$ 13. $\sqrt{94}$

Here are the areas of some squares.
Use the graph to find the length of the side of each square.

14. $18 \, cm^2$ 15. $34 \, cm^2$ 16. $42 \, cm^2$ 17. $66 \, cm^2$ 18. $82 \, cm^2$

Algebra

1. $\triangle = 2\square + 1$

    What is the value of $\triangle$ if:

    $\square = 0, 1, 2, 3, 4$?

2. $\triangle = 3\square - 1$

    What is the value of $\triangle$ if:

    $\square = 1, 2, 3, 4, 5$?

3. $2\triangle = \square + 2$

    What is the value of $\triangle$ if:

    $\square = 2, 4, 6, 8, 10$?

4. $4\triangle = \square - 2$

    What is the value of $\triangle$ if:

    $\square = 2, 6, 10, 14$?

Draw graphs to show:

5. $\triangle = 2\square - 1$

$\square$	1	2	3	4	5
$\triangle$					

6. $\triangle = 3\square + 1$

$\square$	0	1	2	3	4
$\triangle$					

7. $2\triangle = \square + 1$

$\square$	1	3	5	7	9
$\triangle$					

8. $2\triangle = \square - 1$

$\square$	1	3	5	7	9
$\triangle$					

9. Match each line on the graph
   with one of these:

   $\triangle = \square - 1$

   $2\triangle = \square - 2$

   $\triangle = 2\square + 2$

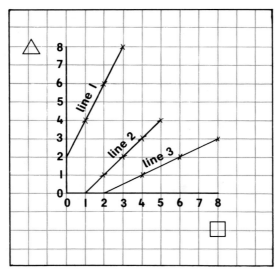

110

Fractions

1. $3\frac{2}{5} + 1\frac{3}{4}$

2. $2\frac{4}{7} + 4\frac{2}{3}$

3. $1\frac{11}{12} + 2\frac{7}{8}$

4. $3\frac{4}{5} - 2\frac{5}{6}$

5. $4\frac{1}{4} - 1\frac{3}{7}$

6. $5\frac{1}{3} - 2\frac{4}{5}$

7. $4\frac{2}{3} \times 1\frac{2}{7}$

8. $1\frac{7}{9} \times 1\frac{1}{8}$

9. $4\frac{1}{5} \times 3\frac{1}{3}$

10. $\frac{4}{9} \div \frac{2}{3}$

11. $\frac{7}{8} \div \frac{3}{4}$

12. $\frac{4}{5} \div \frac{2}{15}$

> **When dividing, mixed numbers must be changed into fractions.**

$$2\frac{1}{4} \div 2\frac{5}{8}$$
$$= \frac{9}{4} \div \frac{21}{8}$$
$$= \frac{\cancel{9}^{3}}{\cancel{4}_{1}} \times \frac{\cancel{8}^{2}}{\cancel{21}_{7}}$$
$$= \frac{6}{7}$$

13. $1\frac{1}{3} \div 1\frac{1}{15}$

14. $2\frac{3}{4} \div 5\frac{1}{2}$

15. $1\frac{2}{3} \div 2\frac{2}{3}$

16. $2\frac{1}{2} \div 3\frac{1}{4}$

17. $1\frac{1}{9} \div 1\frac{1}{4}$

18. $3\frac{1}{8} \div 2\frac{1}{2}$

19. $3\frac{1}{4} \div 1\frac{5}{8}$

20. $1\frac{7}{8} \div 1\frac{1}{4}$

21. $5\frac{1}{4} \div 1\frac{2}{7}$

22. $9\frac{1}{3} \div 1\frac{2}{5}$

23. $2\frac{4}{5} \div 1\frac{13}{15}$

24. $3\frac{3}{4} \div 6\frac{1}{4}$

25. $2\frac{2}{3} \div 1\frac{7}{9}$

26. $4\frac{5}{6} \div 9\frac{2}{3}$

27. $5\frac{3}{5} \div 3\frac{11}{15}$

28. $6\frac{1}{4} \div 4\frac{1}{6}$

29. $5\frac{5}{8} \div 5\frac{5}{6}$

30. $1\frac{7}{9} \div 3\frac{1}{3}$

31. $3\frac{3}{5} \div 7\frac{1}{5}$

32. $1\frac{1}{11} \div 4\frac{4}{5}$

33. $3\frac{5}{6} \div 1\frac{1}{12}$

34. $3\frac{3}{5} \div 1\frac{4}{5}$

35. $3\frac{3}{7} \div 4\frac{4}{5}$

36. $6\frac{2}{3} \div 2\frac{7}{9}$

Ratio

This is the Brindai Safari park.
In the park there are 16 llamas, 10 lions, 8 chimpanzees, 6 tigers and
4 giraffes.

Write the ratio, in its simplest form, of:

1. lions to tigers.
2. tigers to giraffes.
3. lions to giraffes.
4. llamas to lions.
5. chimpanzees to llamas.
6. tigers to chimpanzees.

More animals are to be brought into the park.
How many more lions would you need to make:

7. the ratio of lions to tigers 3:1?
8. the ratio of lions to giraffes 7:2?
9. the ratio of lions to chimpanzees 3:2?

How many more giraffes would you need to make:

10. the ratio of giraffes to llamas 1:2?
11. the ratio of giraffes to chimpanzees 3:2?
12. the ratio of giraffes to lions 6:5?

The number of people who visited the park one Sunday was 5400.
The ratio of adults to children was 1:3.
13. How many of the visitors were adults?
14. How many were children?

Among the adults, the ratio of men to women was 3:2.
15. How many of the visitors were men?
16. How many were women?

Among the children, the ratio of girls to boys was 5:4.
17. How many of the visitors were girls?
18. How many were boys?

In the car park there were 650 vehicles.
Most of the vehicles were cars, but there were buses also.

The ratio of cars to buses was 11:2.
19. How many cars were in the car park?
20. How many buses were there?

Measurement

Calculate the area of each of these shapes.

1.

2.

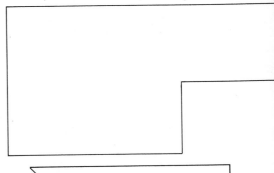

3.

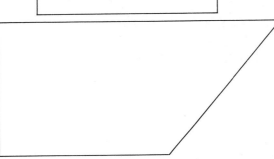

4.

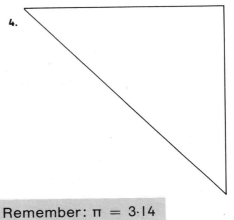

5.

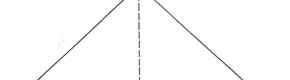

Remember: π = 3·14

6.

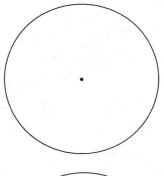

7.

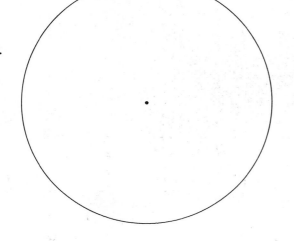

8.

Shape

Compasses, protractor

1. Construct a net to make a solid shape like this.

2. Make a centre point in the middle of your paper.
Mark off radiating lines at 30° intervals.
Make each line 60 mm long.
Make a mark on a line 5 mm from the centre.

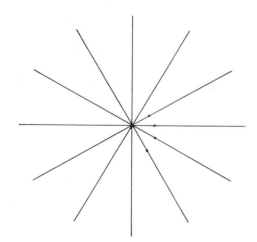

On the next line make a mark 6 mm from the centre.
Continue this, increasing the distance from the centre by I mm each time.
Join the dots to make a **spiral**.

Measurement

2p coin, cotton reel, tube, calipers

Remember: circumference = π × diameter (π = 3·14)

1. Measure the diameter of each object.
   Calculate its circumference.
   Calculate how far each object will roll in 10 revolutions.

2. Mark a starting point.
   Measure how far each object rolls in 10 revolutions.
   Compare your results with your calculations.

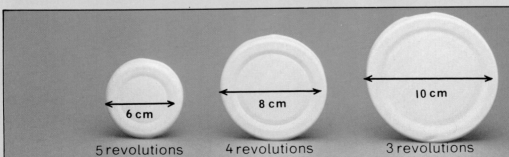

6 cm

8 cm

10 cm

5 revolutions   4 revolutions   3 revolutions

3. Which tin lid will travel a) the furthest distance?   b) the shortest distance?
4. What is the difference in distance travelled between these two?

Number

Here is a different way of multiplying 24 × 36.

 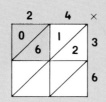 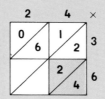 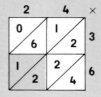

The answer is calculated by adding the diagonal numbers.

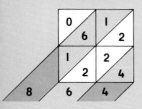

Calculate these in the same way.

 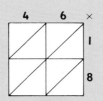  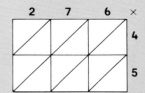

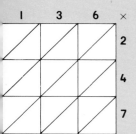 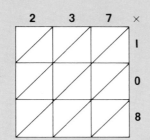 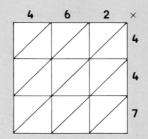

Check your answers with a calculator.
Find out what you can about John Napier 1550–1617.

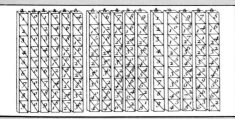

Napier's bones

John Napier

117

Investigations

The digital sum is found by adding the digits of a number.

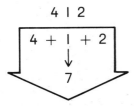

The digital sum of
412 is 7.

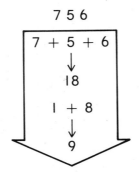

The digital sum of
756 is 9.

Multiplications can be checked by using digital sums.

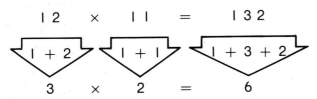

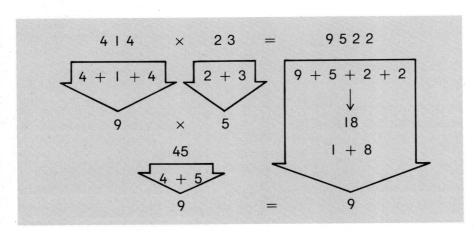

Check these multiplications in the same way.

1. $64 \times 151 = 9664$

2. $429 \times 77 = 33033$

3. $315 \times 41 = 12915$

4. Can division, addition and subtraction be checked by using digital sums?

9 pin geoboard, elastic bands, spotty paper

Record all your results on spotty paper.

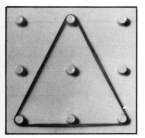 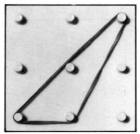 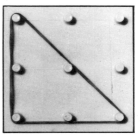

How many different
acute-angled triangles
can you make?

How many different
obtuse-angled triangles
can you make?

How many different
right-angled triangles
can you make?

How many different isosceles triangles can you make?
How many different scalene triangles can you make?
Can you make any equilateral triangles?

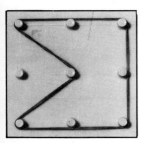 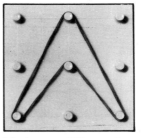

This shape is **concave**.
One of its corners is
"inside" the shape.

Make a different
quadrilateral which
is concave.

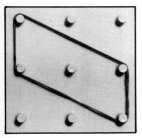 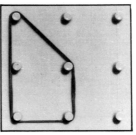

How many different quadrilaterals
can you make which have rotational
symmetry?

How many different quadrilaterals
can you make which have only two
parallel sides?

Pack of playing cards

hearts

clubs

diamonds

spades

1. How many hearts cards are there in a pack?
2. What fraction of the whole pack is this?

3. If you cut a pack of cards 24 times, how many
   times do you think clubs will turn up?
   Do it to see if you were correct.
   Shuffle the pack after each cut.

4. How many aces are there in a pack of cards?
5. What fraction of the whole pack is this?

6. If you cut a pack of cards 26 times, how many
   times do you think an ace will turn up?
   Do it to see if you were correct.
   Shuffle the pack after each cut.

7. If you cut the pack 24 times, how many times
   do you think a red card will turn up?
   Do it to see if you were correct.

Interlocking cm cubes

Use 6 cubes to make shapes with different surface areas.

How many different surface areas can you create?

  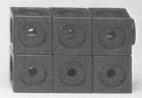

Use 8 cubes to make different shapes.

Find the shapes which have the greatest number of vertices.
Find the shapes which have the least number of vertices.

Use 9 cubes.

What is the largest surface
area you can create?
What is the smallest surface
area you can create?

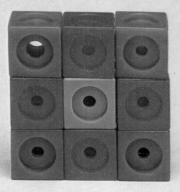

Make a shape like the one above using three different colours of interlocking cubes.

How many different ways can you find of arranging the colours?

You are not allowed to rotate or reflect the same pattern.

Pegboard, pegs

A game for two people.

Aim To put the peg in the bottom left-hand hole.

Only one peg is needed. Choose who goes first.

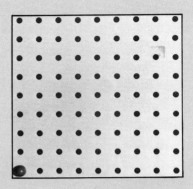

Rules

1. The peg may be put in any hole on the board to begin with.
2. The peg can only be moved to the W, S or SW.
3. The peg can be moved any number of holes.
4. The peg can only be moved in a straight line.
5. Take it in turns to move the peg.

Here is a game being played between Mark and Cathryn.

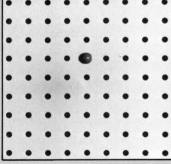

Mark puts the peg here 6 holes along, 7 holes up.

Cathryn may move W, S or SW.

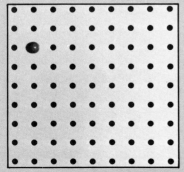

She moves the peg 4 holes W.

Mark may move W, S or SW.

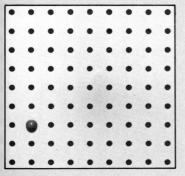

He moves the peg 4 holes S.
Mark is now sure to win.
Can you see why?

When a hole has been used to begin a game, it cannot be used as a starting hole again.

Play the game with your partner.

Play Solitaire
Arrange 24 pegs like this:

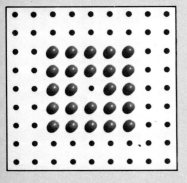

Jump over an adjacent peg into a hole.
Remove the peg you have jumped over.
Try to end with only one peg left on the board.

Polyclops

Polyclops are very friendly creatures and love to talk to each other.
Whilst they talk they always stand on a square grid so that they can see each other.
There are never more than 2 polyclops in a straight line horizontally, vertically or diagonally.

Here is how 6 polyclops can stand and talk on a square grid of 9.

⊙ ⊙ ·

⊙ · ⊙   No more than 2 of them are in a straight line
           in any direction.

· ⊙ ⊙

Can they stand in other positions? If so, draw diagrams to show the positions.

Can another polyclop join them for a talk?

· · · ·

· · · ·   Show how 8 polyclops can stand and
             talk on a square grid of 16.

· · · ·

· · · ·

What is the maximum number of polyclops which can stand and talk on a square grid of 25?

Calculator

Put the decimal point followed by any
five digits on the calculator display.

Aim

To change the number shown on the display to 1 in six moves or less.

Rules

You must use one of the four operations ($+ \times \div -$) followed by a two
digit number to change the number on display.

Here are some examples of two digit numbers.

The symbol 0 must be treated as a digit. You may use a decimal point.
Here is one way of changing 0·49125 into 1 in three moves.

   Enter $\times 80$ into the calculator.

Enter $+0·7$

Enter $\div 40$

Play the game yourself.
Keep a record of the display numbers and the numbers you entered.

Assessment Test

1. Add 17·32, 1·856 and 12·7

2. Find the surface area of this cuboid.

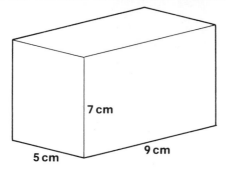

3.   3 9 4
     ×   8 7
     ─────────

4. 2 3) 5 7 0 4

5. Add 36704, 4078, and 92076

6. $1\frac{3}{5} + 4\frac{3}{4}$

7. $7\frac{1}{2} - 2\frac{4}{5}$

8. $4\frac{1}{6} \times 3\frac{3}{5}$

9. $3\frac{1}{9} \div 2\frac{1}{3}$

10. Find the volume of this cylinder.
    (π = 3·14)

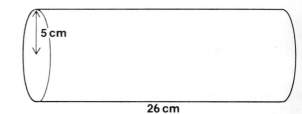

11.   1 4 · 3 2 0
      −   7 · 9 8 4
      ─────────────

12.   1 · 7 8
        × 3 · 4
      ─────────────

13. 4 · 6) 7 2 · 6 8

14. Find the circumference of
    a circle of radius 4 cm.
    (π = 3·14)

15. Choose the most sensible answer.

                    7·99

    $\sqrt{79}$ =   9·02

                    8·89

6. Change these fractions into decimals.
   Give each answer to 3 decimal places.

   a) $3\frac{5}{6}$ b) $4\frac{3}{7}$ c) $6\frac{7}{11}$

7. Match each line on the graph
   with one of these statements.

   $2\triangle = \square - 3$

   $\triangle = 3\square + 1$

   $\triangle = 2\square - 2$

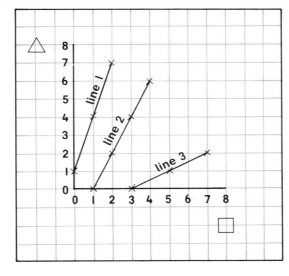

18. At the transport garage there were 306 buses. The ratio of single decker buses to
    double decker buses was 7:11.
    How many single decker buses were there?

19. Write these numbers in full
    a) 5×10^6 b) 4×10^4

20. Give the bearing of each
    town from Osterley.

Dunstone ⊙

Armitage ⊙

N

Osterley

Camberley ⊙

⊙ Binter

21. The cash price of a TV set is £460. $\frac{1}{4}$ of the price was paid as a deposit.
    How much was paid as a deposit?

22. Interest was charged at 8% on the remainder.
    How much interest was charged?

Glossary

bearing — direction of one place from another – measured from north in a clockwise direction

clinometer — instrument for measuring angles of elevation

digital sum — the digital sum of 413 is $4 + 1 + 3 = 8$

ellipse

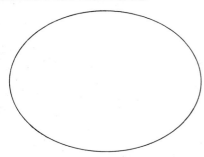

inverse — the inverse of 4 is $\frac{1}{4}$
the inverse of $\frac{1}{3}$ is 3

pi (π) — ratio of circumference to diameter $\quad C = \pi \times d$
ratio of area to radius squared $\quad A = \pi \times r^2$
$\pi = 3\cdot14$

ratio — numerical relationship of quantities
△△△○○
ratio of △s to ○s $= 3 : 2$

reflex angle — any angle between 180° and 360°.

significant figures — the digits which are worth the most.
4123 to one significant figure is 4000

spiral

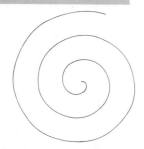

square root (√) — $\sqrt{36} = 6$

surface area — the total area of all the faces of a shape